THE TRANSFORMATION OF THE SCIENTIFIC WORLD VIEW

THE TRANSFORMATION
OF THE SCIENTIFIC
WORLD VIEW

KARL HEIM

. . .

HARPER & BROTHERS PUBLISHERS

NEW YORK

Library of Congress catalog card number: 53-10966

PREFACE

THE volume to which this is a sequel was essentially a philosophical foundation, dealing with the fundamental relationship between the self and the world, and between God, the self, and the world. In this volume attention is focused on particular problems, above all the ones which are raised at the point where natural science, quite involuntarily and by following its own lines of thought, impinges on the region where lies the question about God. This is the case where the fundamental substance of which the world is composed comes into view. Also at the point where the fundamental forms of space and time come into mind. Also where the fundamental law of the world process, namely causality, requires investigation. And finally at the point where man stumbles upon the secret of life.

I wish to express my sincere thanks to those who have contributed, directly or indirectly, to the production of this book. Most of all I must thank Pastor Hans Martin Neidermeier, who has given all the time he could spare from his regular work to the publication of the book; then Dr. Heinrich Hermann, who, as an established expert in the field of modern physics, has given me invaluable help particularly in the parts concerned with physics; and Dr. Otto Kübler for all his cooperation.

Then I must thank all those who have helped to set in a new light the ideas which I have previously put forward in various publications. Among others I would mention Dr. Otto Huppert who, from the technical side, sees the notions of paradox and polarity from a different point of view, and knows how to put them before modern men in a particularly illuminating fashion (cf. his book *Das Unfassbare*). Also Dr. Friedrich Wilhelm Weber who has set paradox in the light of the supra-polar world in the books *Gott in der Natur*

5

and *Der Altböse Feind*, which contain rich and valuable material especially from animal life.

And finally, a word of greeting and thanks to all who have written to me and given me valuable hints and stimuli.

May this book, as it goes out into a greatly confused world, find its way to those who need its help.

KARL HEIM

Tübingen
  May, 1951

CONTENTS

ACKNOWLEDGMENTS

I HAVE greatly profited from the advice of two university colleagues, Professor G. S. Rushbrooke of the Newcastle Division and Professor J. B. Cragg of the Durham Division, who have identified and interpreted for me many technical references in the text. As a general rule I have not felt at liberty to indicate where, in their judgment or my own, the argument is open to question. Nor have I tried to produce alternative references to English works of science or philosophy at the places where Professor Heim falls back on technical German books and articles. The book was written in the German intellectual context, and any attempt to domesticate it within the English context would, I think, only impair its quality. I am grateful, too, to Miss Vera M. Neill of St. Aidan's Society in the University of Durham for her interest and practical help. It has not been considered necessary to produce a subject-index for this book because sufficient guidance is given in the table of contents.

W. A. WHITEHOUSE

University of Durham
June, 1952

I

INTRODUCTION

1. THE STARTING-POINT FOR THE ANALYSIS OF FAITH AND NATURAL SCIENCE

If we wish to investigate the relation between faith in God and the theses of modern natural science, we require an origin from which to plot the enquiry, just as a circle must have its origin immovably fixed in order that its circumference may be plotted in a given plane. The fixed point from which we must begin can be none other than God. For nothing other than God is given to us men as thus fixed. But how are we to get to this origin? Here is a question which today is a matter for heated debate. To reach this fixed origin, it would seem desirable to offer a definition of the notion of God. To this end, one might proceed either from the dogmatic formulations of a particular church, or from a brief survey of the history of religion in which the notion of God has assumed ever-changing forms. Or one might begin from a religious-philosophical system with a notion of the Absolute and Eternal, as something which stands above all formulations both in the history of religion and in the confessions of churches, and take this as an abstract indication of what we want. But all these proposals would plunge us at once into an endless and sterile struggle between current theological trends, or else they would lure us into a carefully guarded neutrality as between the contending parties in the Church's confessional struggles, and thereby oblige us to proceed from a mere abstraction remote from life.

By none of these routes shall we come to an immovable fixed point from which to begin drawing the circle, and, with this as centre, describe its circumference so as to cover the

11

whole field. The intention of this book would be better expressed by the proposal to leave on one side all notions drawn from theology or religious philosophy, and to begin instead with the simple but forceful answer which Luther gives to the question 'What does it mean to have a God, or what is God?', in the course of explaining the first commandment in the Large Catechism. For this answer stands not only above all confessional distinctions, but also above the differences between all religions. It is therefore a suitable basis for analysis for men of all religions. Luther's answer has at the same time the further advantage that I cannot express it in the form of a dogma, but only in the form of a confession behind which stands my whole personal life. This simple answer of Luther, a classic of its kind, reads as follows:

A God is that to which we look for all good and where we resort for help in every time of need. Therefore to have a God is simply to trust and believe in one with our whole heart; as I have often said, the confidence and faith of the heart make both God and an idol. . . . For the two, faith and God, have inevitable connection. Now, I say, whatever your heart clings to and confides in, that is really your God.

The meaning of the first commandment according to Luther is therefore this. God says: 'Let me alone be your God . . . and when you are in need or distress, flee to me and cleave to me. I will give you what suffices, and help in all your need. Only don't let your heart cleave to any other nor rest in any other.'

This passage is the more important for our own time in that Luther is not merely addressing the members of some particular church. Luther is also dealing in this context with the people whom one meets today in increasing numbers, who say: 'I don't in the least understand what these words are supposed to mean. I lack any religious sense. I have no relation whatever to the whole world of religion, and never have had. I am like a completely unmusical person, who remains quite unmoved though someone is playing to him

Bach's most powerful fugue.' Luther refuses to let this explanation stand. According to Luther, every man has in himself that which is the essence of faith in God. 'No people has ever been so impious that it has not set up and practised some kind of divine worship.' Even if some day it were the case that all forms of divine worship disappeared from the earth, there would none the less still be some kind of form wherein was made manifest that which makes up the essence of faith in God. Luther reminds us above all of what for most men is a substitute for true faith in God: money or property, power, cleverness, good reputation. 'Whoever has money and property trusts in them, and boasts in them proudly and securely. He surely has a god, called Mammon, that is money and property, on whom he sets his whole heart. He who has money and property deems himself secure, he is happy and fearless as if he were in the midst of Paradise. He who has nothing doubts and despairs, as though he knew of no god. For you will find very few persons who are of a cheerful heart when they have not Mammon. This thing cleaves to our natures until we are in our graves. Therefore any man who trusts and presumes upon his great skill, cleverness, power, influence, friends or reputation, has indeed a god. . . . Notice again how presumptuous, proud and secure these people become in regard to such possessions, and how despondent when without them or deprived of them. Therefore I repeat that to have a god means to have something in which the heart completely trusts.'

To Luther, therefore, it belongs to our essential self to accept the hypothesis that something exists upon which we may rely unconditionally, which is absolutely secure, to which we commit ourselves not merely with the mind or with the will, but to which we cleave with our whole heart; a truth expressed later by Matthias Claudius when he said 'Man must have something constant'. Faith, therefore, is the relationship in which the human self stands to some reality which is taken to be absolutely constant. Here, then, Luther and Claudius make an assertion about the self of every man which is not strictly demonstrable, but which counts on every man's assent. In the discussion of fundamentals in a previous volume[1] we suggested that the self cannot be objectified. We cannot posit our self to ourselves so as to make an assertion about it, and yet this self is directly confided to us. We are better acquainted with it than with any objective thing. And yet we can only talk about it imprecisely and figuratively. For this very reason, what Luther says to us here is directly intelligible. We understand what he means when he says, using figurative language, that we are obliged to cleave to something with our whole heart; and again, that when some such thing is given to us we stand in the world happy, fearless, proud and confident, feeling ourselves to be in Paradise, or alternatively that we are full of gloom and misgiving if we are deprived of such an anchorage. If Luther is right in making this existential statement, a further consequence follows. If there should be a reality so constant that our whole heart can cleave to it, however great the load of distress and sorrow with which it is burdened, then it must have an absolute constancy. It cannot, therefore, belong to polar[2] space, for it pertains to the structure of that space that nothing can be absolutely constant. Everything which affords an anchorage can only do so in that it itself is held by something else, and so on to infinity, in accordance with the principle ' *Teneo quia teneor*—I hold because I am held '. A reality to which in truth we can cleave with our whole heart can only be one which we believe is not subject to this fundamental law of our ' polar ' world, one which is not a member of the infinite regress, and is therefore a ' supra-polar ' reality. Of such a reality alone can Luther say: ' The heart may know no comfort or confidence other than in him, and may not be torn from him; rather on this let it venture and stake everything which is on earth.'

This reality, which is unconditionally constant, cannot consist in a plurality but only in a unity. All things, all entities, which are present in a multiplicity, exert a mutual pressure

---

[1] The reference is to *Christian Faith and Natural Science* (S.C.M. Press, 1953).

[2] The term ' polar ' is introduced in the previous volume, and there it is fully discussed in Section 13. It refers to that all-pervasive feature of the perceptible world whereby reality is constituted from the play of opposing forces, the weaker giving way eventually to the stronger.

upon one another. They act concurrently with one another. Each limits the other's sphere of life. This mutual limitation is characteristic of existence in the polar world. It follows, therefore, that there can be only one supra-polar being, existing in numerical singularity, to which we can cleave with our whole heart. Why this being should not be a thing, but always and only a person, I sought to establish in the volume on fundamentals in the course of discussing the question of God. There can never be true polytheism, therefore, but only polydemonism. All the beings which man wants to put alongside God are not gods. They can only be demons with limited powers. If this is the case, then two possibilities alone lie open to us men in respect of the question about God. Either there is nothing at all in which we can place our unconditional trust, nothing therefore in which we believe. There are only things with which we can come reasonably to terms by making careful calculations about what we are able to see and touch. Or there is the second possibility which is faith, the relationship in which we stand with one to whom our whole heart cleaves. This possibility, which is something more than reckoning with objectively given things by technical or medical art, is something which lies completely outside the realm of polar space. Access to the 'one', beside whom there is no other, cannot be achieved by any kind of causal reaction out of our polar world. It can only be granted to us through grace, and the response to this gift of grace can only consist in this, that we surrender ourselves to it with our whole heart, that we love it with our whole heart, with our whole soul, with our whole strength, and with all our powers.

If these two possibilities, the only two which are properly open in respect of the question about God, were to be clearly displayed on the historical plane, no more wars would flare up between different religions, like those which have cost so much blood. There would be no instances of fanatical religious persecution, and no ideological battles. There seems, however, to be a third position. What is the content of this third possibility? There have been men who have not yet been able to participate in the grace of access to the 'one' to which we have entrusted ourselves. And yet there is a lively obligation within them which Luther says can find quiescence only through faith; the desire of the heart to cleave to something or other. Thus they try, by their own resources, to satisfy this obligation, so far as is possible within the polar world. They come then to the point of treating relative magnitudes as absolute; and therefore to an attempt to believe in something with which man is able to come to terms by his own technical resources from a basis of observation. Thus we are faced with the illusion against which the first commandment is solely and properly directed. Pure godlessness or pure infidelity, taken in itself, is not a counter-attack directed against faith in God. It is only a negative attitude, a privation of the gift of grace which makes it possible for a man not only to do his technical reckonings but also really to believe. The only thing which is rebellion against God is the effort to reduce to rest the restless movement among the limitless series of relative magnitudes by some convulsive exertion, and to raise some creaturely magnitude to the rank of suprapolar reality.

2. THE SUBJECT-MATTER OF THE ANALYSIS

In the previous section we have determined the point which must be immovably fixed in order that the circle to be traced in this book may have its location; the point to which it is rooted in order that its wide arc may be drawn over the region of natural science. Now we want to bring into clear view a second thing with which this book is concerned: the region within the circle which is to be described by its arc radiating from the fixed origin. The question is about the material of this analysis to which our entire investigation is devoted.

Some time ago, one of our leading scientists, Pascual Jordan, one of the first exponents of quantum mechanics, wrote as follows: 'We are not living in an age of religious fruitfulness —we have neither a Luther nor a Francis. Nor are we living in an age of artistic fruitfulness. In the outlook of modern man there is only one spiritual phenomenon characteristic of our age and at the same time of unqualified magnitude and power. Our epoch has found the authentic symbol of its inner struggle in the researches of natural science.' It is with this spiritual phenomenon, which gives to our age its unique status among all ages, that we intend to occupy ourselves in this volume. But we do not look upon it as does the scientific worker himself, in so far as he remains within the frontiers of this region of enquiry, namely as a step forward in pure scientific knowledge. If a layman wants to come to terms with the conclusions of contemporary physics and biology, we must refer him to the latest books of the experts, among which he will find some which are intelligible even to laymen. Here, however, we have set ourselves another task. We propose to look at this mighty spiritual phenomenon, of which Pascual Jordan spoke, exclusively in the light of the question about God.

If one asks what is the bearing on the question about God of the transformation of the scientific view of the world with which we are confronted today, one receives as a rule this kind of answer. Even in natural science, we are near the end of atheism, near to the 'liquidation of materialism' such as governed scientific thought in the days of Ernst Haeckel or Virchow. The collapse of a causal-mechanical world-picture has again made room for God. Well-known scientists have committed themselves to the view that the marvellous con- stitution of the world's structure not only permits the infer- ence of an intelligent Creator but invites such an inference. It is widely held, therefore, that the significance of the current transformation in the scientific world view is this: that the line of approach from nature to God which was pursued by men of the Enlightenment and Rationalism, but which was blocked in the age of causal mechanism, is now open again following upon the breakdown of the causal-mechanical world- view. Is this a true perception of the meaning of the prodi- gious events which concern us here?

If we are to deal with this question with firm ground be- neath our feet, not, that is to say, by trusting to our own insecure experience, but by attending to the Bible, we shall have to reckon with an impressive passage in the first chapter of the Epistle to the Romans, where we are told that we have no excuse if we repudiate a knowledge of God from His works. Here in this chapter, if anywhere, we must discover an answer to the question about how one may find an approach from the created world to its Creator. Therefore, although it is not within the scheme of the book to engage in biblical exposition which is an obligation for theologians, a few pages must be devoted to the exposition of this chapter. For this chapter is of fundamental significance for our enquiry. A false exposition of it has produced much confusion in the analytical discussion of natural science and Christianity. It has always been supposed that this is the biblical passage with which contemporary atheism, materialism, secularism and nihilism, must be strongly opposed; for these views, held on all sides today, merit the judgment that men are inexcusable if they harden themselves haughtily against God at a time when He reveals His power so marvellously in natural events. But we must ask whether this is really the meaning of the chapter. Is it really directed against atheism such as we have today? Is it really to be taken as meaning that the men against whom it is directed have refused to draw the conclusion of a Creator from the created works? We are dealing with the meaning of the sentences in verses 18 and 19, in which Paul establishes the inexcusable guilt of the heathen world, and thus supplies a motive for God's judgment upon the heathen world. 'For what can be known about God is plain to them, because God has shown it to them.' The question is this. Does Paul mean that since the creation of the world, God has made Himself so clearly known uninterruptedly in His created works, that we incur inexcusable guilt if we do not see the Creator, and therefore consider Him to be unreal? Is this passage dealing in fact with the denial of God as the intrinsic guilt of the heathen world? This exposition of the Pauline passage is the one adopted almost universally today among celebrated theologians (for instance, by Paul Althaus, *Der Brief an die Römer*, p. 14, Göttingen, 1933). It is the one which naturally occurs to us on a first reading of verse 18. If, therefore, we venture to deviate from this customary interpretation, it will be necessary to establish carefully the ground for such deviation. The

main reason for it is the only one to be advanced here. It is
found in the context in which the sentence occurs. It so
happens that what we call atheism is not mentioned again in
the whole of the rest of the chapter, and therefore that the
idea we expect is not further developed, namely that man is
guilty of gross self-delusion if he represses a conclusion which
his intellect is bound to draw when he studies nature, and
thereby heedlessly ignores a manifest and obvious reality.
This atheism, of which there were sporadic representatives
among the philosophers even in the time of Paul, is certainly
not the matter under discussion. The inexcusable guilt which
Paul says the heathen have incurred is that of a tremendous
confusion (note the Greek words *allattein* and *metallattein*);
the confusion or exchange of some part of the visible transient
creation with the invisible intransient eternal God. The
guilt of which Paul here accuses the heathen is that of making
a confusion between two realities which are in conflict with
one another and can never be brought into line, which confusion and interchange brings our whole thought and life
into hopeless chaos. Paul subsequently illustrates this by
reference to the fatal aberration in sexual life which comes
to expression in homosexuality in the case both of men and of
women. Paul's use of this illustration shows precisely and
clearly that the guilt of which he speaks consists in the confusion of things which may never be exchanged for one another without creating a chaotic situation.

The radical denial of God which is familiar to us today did
indeed come to occasional expression in antiquity. Think,
for instance, of Lucretius and his disciples. But this late product of classical culture could never have merited so explicit
a refutation as is here deemed necessary by Paul. Atheism
was as remote from the broad mass of men in that age as it is
from the average citizen in India or Japan today. The men
of that time were not atheists; they were religious to a degree.
Paul says as much to them in Acts 17.23, where he is impressed
by the wealth of temples and the costly cultus which Athens
boasted at the Parthenon.

They were as taken up with heathen idolatry in all its forms
and as religiously intoxicated as are people in India today on

the night of the Shiwa festival, for instance, when the image
of the god is carried in and the frenzy reaches its height.
There still today we have a demonstration of the intimate
relation between religious intoxication and chaotic aberrations
in sexual life. It was this polytheism against which Paul here
waged his passionate warfare. In contrast to relativism and
nihilism, it was the highest conceivable peak of making
creaturely objects absolute. It is taken as established in
polytheism that behind natural forces like the sun, the snow-
storm, or the thunder, there is something numinous which
man may track down and elucidate. For the polytheist that is
not open to debate. But the question generally at stake here,
which Paul tries to have out explicitly with the heathen, is the
one indicated by the fundamental Commandment of the Old
Testament: 'I am the Lord thy God. Thou shalt have no
other gods beside me.' The Old Testament says again and
again: 'The Lord our God is a jealous God.' The Old Testament does not range itself against doubt about God or against
godlessness. This plays only a small part in the Old Testament. 'The fool', it observes, 'says in his heart: there is no
God.' But it does range itself with all passion against that
Absolute which would put itself alongside God. Such an
Absolute alongside God is, for instance, the human self, which
puts itself on the throne and prescribes for itself autonomously
the law of its conduct. Another Absolute is an absolute
human ruler, not appointed by God. Every such Absolute
takes away from God a measure of His own absoluteness. God,
according to Luther's declaration, is that wherein we place our
entire confidence, that which is our sole refuge in all our need,
that which we should love with all our heart and soul and
strength and all our powers. If there is a second Absolute,
set alongside God, it takes out of our hearts some part of the
sovereign power of God, some part of the unconditional confidence and entire love which we owe to God. According to
Luther, therefore, to believe in such an Absolute is not mere
godlessness, but a movement of rebellion against God, and
therefore an alliance with an idol.

If this is correct, then we have to do with the question of
God and of the opposition between Him and every kind of

idolatry which seeks to demolish His sole Lordship, not merely in the history of religion, but over all fields of experience and enquiry including philosophy and natural science. Thus there is not simply a direct way which leads up to God from natural events, the *via causalitatis* pursued by the older apologists. This direct way leads, not to God, but to a higher form of divinized creature. The only way which really leads to God is the indirect, or negative way. This indirect way is marked by the collapse, over all fields of life and thought, of the Absolutes which stand as hindrances in the way of God's sole Lordship. An illustration of what is involved can be drawn from the world powers which rise one after another out of the sea of world history, as the Book of Daniel indicates; each one, as it comes to the zenith of its power, is tempted to divinize its ruler. As soon as they reach this point, they stand in the way of God's sole Lordship. The road to faith in the true God proceeds then not only by the believing man seeing through this glorification of the ruler beforehand as the divinizing of a creature; God's sole Lordship and complete sovereignty may come to expression in even stronger form, in the fact that these great powers rise one after another from the sea of history, and sink back into it just as quickly after their short flowering. This repeated collapse of every earthly imperialism is the most impressive demonstration of the fact that no divinization of any earthly power can stand, that every absolutizing of any earthly absolute always carries within itself the seeds of death. God sets up His throne on the wreckage of human earthly thrones, and the history of the world is strewn with the wreckage of demolished imperialisms and smashed altars, whose debris reveals impressively the sole Lordship of God.

We can carry over this law which obtains in world history in another form into the field of natural science. Wherever, in the description of nature, an absolute is posited; wherever a magnitude is postulated which needs no other magnitude through which it exists, but which exists only through itself, or wherever a form of existence is presupposed which needs no other form of existence to which it is relative, but which has validity solely through itself, there faith breaks into scientific description, though the word 'faith' or the word 'God' does not occur.   For the subjective function fulfilled by such an absolute is that mentioned by Luther in the Large Catechism, when he speaks of that in which we trust unconditionally and to which we wholly commit ourselves. This function of unconditional trust is not only possible with respect to an invisible personality whom we portray to ourselves as a Father enthroned in heaven.   It can also come into play with respect to a magnitude which can only be expressed abstractedly.

An illustration can be given of how such a mathematical magnitude can take on a religious character.   The plan which an architect produces rests on the assumption that the axioms of Euclidean geometry, and of the statics which depend on it, are absolutely valid.   If the validity of these axioms were to be shattered; if, for instance, the statement were open to question that the shortest distance between two points is the straight line joining them, and if in fact the shortest distance between them were a curved line (as is the case in spherical space), then the whole calculation of building materials necessary for the job would have to be altered, and the estimated cost would be different from what was originally planned. The architect, therefore, must include in his reckoning a factor which is not proved but has to be accepted in faith, if all his calculations are not to be based on mere chance.   The geometrical axioms and the laws of statics bound up with them are not capable of further proof.   They must, however, hold for the future which as yet we cannot see.   Every proof of these fundamental assumptions is a vicious circle, assuming in the end the validity of what it purports to prove.   Gifted but hypercritical master-builders, like the one who built the tower of Ulm Cathedral, have sometimes experienced a real struggle for faith by reason of the insecurity of these fundamentals.   They have had sleepless nights, contemplating the catastrophe that must follow if their calculations contained an insecure factor.   From this it is evident that wherever an absolute factor has to be accepted, in the description of nature or in calculations, what is fundamentally a religious faith breaks into scientific reckoning.   It is necessary to put one's confidence in some absolute or other. The ultimate object of this confidence can only be, either God, who is alone capable of giving us an eternal anchorage, or an idol, which tears us down into the abyss. From this example, drawn from the structure of Euclidean space, we see precisely how matters stand in respect of that absolute with which we reckon in practical life. Three possibilities are always available. The first is that we take the absolute, with all the consequences entailed by it, without any reflection as something simply given. It stands as something which in general is valid. No one has questioned it. The second possibility is that faith in this absolute has already suffered some kind of blow. It is comparable to a ruler who still occupies his throne, but the throne is already beginning to totter. The third possibility is that the absolute loses its validity. This does not happen by theoretical developments purely, and therefore not because speculative reason establishes that there is no cogent logical proof of the universal validity of the absolute in question. Such purely theoretical reflections have no real destructive power. In themselves they can only be of equal subjectivity and relativity, and may themselves be robbed of power by an opposite kind of speculation. The fact that so impressive a power as that of Napoleon's sovereignty, or Hitler's, was subject to the law of corruption in all earthly things, and that therefore there can be no talk about the eternity of these empires, was clear enough for a long time to all thinking men, in a theoretical way. But this theoretical insight was not enough to push the tyrant off the throne. The claim to be absolute, which was accepted in regard to such potentates, was first invalidated in the moment when, through a brute fact of experience, the throne on which they had sat collapsed for all men to see. From such instances we derive the rule governing the fate of all such mighty ones who, for a decade, a century, or a millennium, have reckoned themselves to be absolute. And this rule we must apply also to the absolute magnitudes which, for centuries or for millennia, have held their place in man's view of nature as self-evident and unquestioned elements. With the relevant modifications, the fundamental commandment applies also in the field of natural science: 'I am the Absolute, and thou shalt have no other absolutes beside me.' Every magnitude in which we put our whole trust, to whatever realm it pertains, stands in the way of the absoluteness of God, because we place in it confidence such as is due to God alone.

Now at last we are able to answer the question which has been in view through all these considerations. What is the significance of the inner transformation which has taken place in contemporary natural science, if that transformation be considered not merely from the point of view of scholarship, but in relation to the question of God? Wherein does the revolution consist which has taken place before our eyes in modern science, particularly in physics? Manifestly in a 'twilight of the gods', involving on a large scale one after another of the absolutes which have held their own unquestioned for centuries. They have collapsed together, and not by reason of any theoretical reflections of the kind which were advanced in the earlier period of scepticism and relativism, but rather through facts of experience verified experimentally and not to be denied, although they were in clear contradiction to dogmatic principles with which men had hitherto approached the study of nature, and although the experiments by which they were established were of an unlooked-for kind.

Three such absolutes are pre-eminently involved. The first is the *absolute object*, by which I mean the hypothesis that there is an objective matter of fact which has a completely determinate structure and constitution, completely independent of any other subject, and therefore independent of the point of view of an observer or experimenter.

The second is *absolute space and absolute time*. This was the ultimate hypothesis upon which the whole of classical physics was built according to Newton's fundamental work.

The third is the *absolute determination of the world process*, by which I mean the hypothesis that the course of world events is absolutely established because it is subject to the universally valid law of causality, according to which one event follows necessarily from preceding events. According to Laplace, an omniscient spirit, capable of seeing nature in its entirety at any moment, could argue backwards to everything which has ever happened, and predict exactly everything which is yet to happen.

We know instinctively that these three absolutes are of decisive importance for the question of God. If any one of them were to be invalidated, it would seem to us at first glance as though the whole universe and all its ordinances had been imperilled as though by an earthquake. If there is no absolute object, and everything we see is conditioned by the subject, then there is nothing in which we can put our unconditional trust. We can never make a statement expressing something which is true of all things and can claim universal validity. Real life and dreams fuse together suddenly, and there is nothing constant to which we can hold fast.

The same is true of the second absolute, absolute space and absolute time. Only if we live in a space whose measure and regularities are fixed do we feel really safe in this world. It is not an accident that the medieval Church could accept the Copernican revolution without resistance, for that revolution only involved new courses for the stars within the same fixed universal space as before. Space and time themselves kept their measure and order. It was not until Giordano Bruno's attack on space itself, which implied that it had no centre and therefore no boundaries, that the Church felt the blow as of an earthquake which made its foundations tremble. The man who entertained this foolhardy notion must die at the stake, a danger to the Church and a menace to faith in God.

The destruction of the old conviction that the course of events is absolutely determined by the law of causality is equally serious. Oswald Spengler realized the strong religious importance of this fundamental conviction. He took it to be the profane expression of the elementary fact which faith intends to affirm when it clings to predestination in face of all possible doubts. This religious determinism is rendered precarious once the law of causation loses its unconditional significance.

If now we look back upon the course of our argument up to this point, we see that everything which has been said can be taken back to the biblical principle: 'I am the Lord thy God; thou shalt have no other gods beside me', or, more generally, 'I am the Absolute, and thou shalt have no other absolutes beside me'.   The notion of an absolute thus has an all-embracing meaning for all departments of life and thought. It can be applied, as we have seen, to a person just as well as to a mathematical magnitude (think of the example from statics of a constant which an architect must take as given). It may be a fundamental rule of practice, as happens when it is incorporated into the foundations of ethics.   It can also be applied to a logical axiom, upon which we attempt to build a philosophical system.   The thing which necessarily belongs to an absolute, in whatever diverse contexts we employ the word, is the contrast in which it stands to all relatives. Spinoza defined absolute substance as the substance which exists only through itself, needing nothing else in order to exist (*et nulla alia re eget ad existendum*).   This simplest form of employing the concept needs to be amplified.   This law of the absolute, that it is through itself alone, applies not only to its existence, but equally to everything else that can be said about it.   It holds equally of the numerical value or the dimensionality which it presents.   And in what has been said it has become clear that wherever the mysterious and comprehensive notion of the absolute is employed, whether in a theoretical or a practical sense, we are confronted with the question of God. In the last resort there are only two kinds of men, two points of view, two kinds of conviction, which are opposed to one another: those for which there is an absolute, and those who know only relative values and realities.   In respect of this ultimate Either/Or, all other antitheses are secondary.   In respect of this fundamental antithesis which divides the spirits, all other differences in meaning have only a relative significance.

Within these perspectives we shall try to bring together in a coherent whole the decisive questions raised in contemporary natural science about such matters as subject and object, space and time, and determinism in the course of world events.

II

THE ABSOLUTE OBJECT

3. MATERIALISM AS A RELIGIOUS FAITH

On June 28th, 1948, *Pravda,* the central organ of the Communist Party in Russia, published a series of titles for scientific lectures directed against the widespread revival of religious 'superstitions', and among them was this: 'Every religion contradicts science.' For the overthrowing of religious faith, scientific workers were summoned to give lectures about the construction of the universe, the origin of the sun and the earth, the origin of man, the biological sources of plant growth and so forth. In much the same sense, Professor Togerow wrote in the army newspaper *Red Star*: 'The relics of religious faith must be wiped out by systematic scientific propaganda.' The significant thing about these Press notices from the East is this, that here is not just a battle about a proper world-view, with an irreligious version of the world and its process set against religious faith. The point of view presupposed by the titles is that the matter no longer calls for discussion. It will be enough if the generally accepted scientific facts established by research are made known to people. The religious notions, which are all that remain from *bourgeois* days, will then disappear of themselves, like phantoms of the night when the day dawns.

There is no room for doubt that the materialistic interpretation of the facts which it is proposed to present cannot be reconciled with the Christian interpretation. But this does not mean that the materialistic version, as hitherto represented, had nothing to do with religion, so that all religious concepts and ideas must vanish of themselves when the conclusions of natural science are presented in a materialistic light.   On the contrary.   Materialism, as we see it here, is itself a religion.   It is a religious faith in the full sense of the word, having in itself all the marks of a religious faith, only that the content, the thing in this religion on which men put all their confidence, is opposed to what we alone should trust according to the first commandment of the Decalogue.   The religious substance of this faith must therefore be branded as an idol from the Christian point of view.   The very power with which materialism opposes Christianity today, and the deep roots which it has put down in the human soul, would be quite unintelligible if it were not the case that for millions of people it takes the same place in their lives as does belief in God among the Christian community.   Why has materialism got this character of a religious faith, although it rules out faith in a personal God?   The answer does not lie in any vain attempt to combine faith in a personal God with a materialistic view of nature.

No less a man than Newton, the genial creator of classical physics, combined faith in an omnipotent Creator and World-ruler with a mechanical explanation of the world.   How he did so becomes clear, perhaps, through a well-known story which is told about him.   In Newton's study there stood a big new model of the heavens, by which he was able to demonstrate the movement of the sun, the planets and the moons.   A friend of his, who was an atheist, came into the room and stood before the model amazed.   He asked: 'Who has made this?'   Newton looked him straight in the eye and said: 'Nobody.'   What he implied, of course, was that the miraculous structure of the solar system, in which everything moves harmoniously according to eternal laws, cannot have come into being of itself.   Only a creating Spirit can have thought it out, and made it, and kept it in being to this day.

This combination of faith in God and exact natural science, which is at once illuminating to a simple man without further argument, was soon broken up, however, shortly after Newton's time, and prepared the way for the atheism of the French Encyclopedists.   Why, in spite of Newton, do we stand to this day in the presence of an irreconcilable contradiction? To understand this, we must look at the thing which has been the deepest essence of true materialism, ever since the materialistic explanation of the world took its rise in Greek antiquity. The atoms of which, according to Democritus, the world consists, are the immutable and indestructible elements of the cosmos. 'Nothing exists except atoms and empty space. Everything else is opinion.' The atoms from which everything else is built are able to retain their original immutable geometrical structure unaltered through all changes. They can be separated, and joined to one another again. They can enter into different relations with one another. But in all these situations, the atoms themselves remain unalterable. They are not created. They are there through themselves. They were from eternity, and they cannot be annihilated. They are not worn down or incapacitated by the course of time. They cannot grow old. All processes in the nature of corporeal things consist always simply in this, that these unalterable elements experience new separations and new combinations over and over again. This great faith in the immutable eternity of the atoms first came to expression in the work of Leucippus and Democritus, and lives on in the poem of Lucretius, *De Rerum Natura,* and later still in Gassendi. The motions of the atoms are of course achieved in the flux of time, but because the laws of these motions (that of action and reaction, and the later law of gravitation) are grounded in the being of the atoms, these motions also have a share in the eternity of matter and proceed by eternal laws. If we think these great and bold ideas through to their end, we can see why they rule out the biblical faith in God quite radically. As the Bible puts it, God is He who 'alone has immortality'. God is God simply because He alone is eternal. All things or essences other than God are inherently temporal, and exist therefore only in the present moment. Their fate in the next moment is not yet decided. They have no power in themselves to endure from this moment into the next. Left to themselves, they would without God fall back into their non-existence. God, who *alone* has immortality, is able to hold temporal beings like ourselves over the Void, and carry

us over from one moment to the next.   Creatures like ourselves can only become eternal inasmuch as God permits us
to participate in His eternity.   If this is the case, then any
attribution of eternity to a creature is rebellion against God,
and an attempt to cast down from His throne the God who
alone is eternal.   From the standpoint of faith in God, it is a
matter of complete indifference whether a human soul should
claim this eternity himself, and say to the raging sea-billows:
'I am eternal and I defy your might', or whether this titanic
claim be made for an atom.

The material atoms, it would seem, must be eternal; for if
they were not from eternity, whence can they have been
derived?   How can they have come to be there?   Because, on
this hypothesis, there is nothing except what is material, the
atoms can only exist through themselves.   The material atom
must at some stage have brought itself out of the Void.   But
such an origination of matter out of nothing would be an act
of creation just as wonderful and incomprehensible as that
professed in any of the other religions.   Alternatively, the
atoms must have been produced by something which itself is
material in the same way.   This must have been produced by
something else, and this again by something else, and so on to
infinity.   We should thus reach an infinite series of origins.
An infinity which has no beginning is identical with something which is from eternity.   Faith in the eternity of matter
belongs to the essence of true materialism, and everywhere
comes to be acknowledged as its fundamental dogma, provided
one treats it as a serious conviction and thinks it through to
its end, instead of merely treating it as a superficial label.
But this fundamental dogma at once gives to materialism the
character of a religious belief.   If the atoms, and the laws by
which they move themselves, are eternal, then we can put
complete confidence in them.   We can apply to them the
remark made by Matthias Claudius: 'Man must have something constant to which he can anchor himself, something
which does not depend on him, but on which he depends.
The anchor must hold the ship.   For if the ship drags her
anchor, her course will miscarry, and disaster lies near.'
This 'constant', which as materialists we believe ourselves

to possess in matter, does not lie in the fact that a particular form of matter, say a piece of iron, or a corner-stone in the foundation of a house, stays unconditionally fixed when subject to pressure or strain.

The fixed matter can therefore be nothing else than the absolute object, given from beyond ourselves, and completely independent of ourselves, or of any other subject. It does not depend upon our discovering it. It is what it is through itself alone, without reference to or dependence on the impression we have of it, or the kind of picture we make of it. All our sense perceptions, and our concepts, are directed towards this objective thing. The object itself, however, remains in sovereign independence, beyond all our perceptions and presentations. And this brings us to a second point where it is clear that materialism is a religious faith.

Only by observation and experience can we establish that there is an absolute object which is not a dream, not a phantom, but a reality. If we also suppose that we are able to see this absolute object with our eyes and grasp it with our hands, that is, of course, an error. What we receive through sight and touch is always only a subjective impression or a complex of sense perceptions. To say that on the further side of this phenomenal world, as Kant called it, there is a 'thing in itself', is pure faith. It is a bolder faith than the faith Idealism has in the existence and eternity of the self, against which no clear contradiction could be established in the era of classical physics, though philosophical doubts could be raised. For we have direct information of some kind about the self. Descartes wrote in his first *Meditation: Cogito ergo sum*—from the function of thinking, about which I know, I am able to conclude that I am. This is not the case with our knowledge of objective matter. Here we are obliged to reach out, in bold faith, beyond the whole world of phenomena, and apprehend that beyond all our experience of sight and touch there is something which we cannot see, but which nevertheless is there. But materialist faith is not only bolder than idealist faith in the self; it is also more precarious than believing in a 'thou' whom I do not see confronting me, though I am aware of his proximity in some mysterious way.   When I have attained this faith in an unseen 'thou', however, it is only a step from the human 'thou' to the eternal 'Thou'.   For to believe in the loyalty of a man is to make a leap of confidence to an 'I' whom I do not see, in whom I nevertheless put my trust on the ground of such love as I have experienced from him.   From there it is only one more step to trust in an eternal 'Thou'.   But materialist faith goes beyond this faith in my own self, and this faith in an invisible 'thou', when it prescribes belief in an unperceivable which lies in complete independence outside all sense impressions and all experience of a 'thou' to which I have direct access.   The objective thing we call matter needs no subject and no observer for its existence.   It goes on existing when no faculty of knowledge is directed upon it.   This is what we mean by the expression 'the absolute object'.   The objects with which we have to do all the time in everyday life are only relative objects; objects, that is to say, which are correlative to a subject. Such an object is conditioned by a subject observing the object from its own standpoint.   It is an object relative to this subject.   The absolute object stands, in distinction from this, as that which is conditioned by no subject at all.

4. THE REDUCTION OF MATTER INTO ENERGY AND LIGHT

The decisive characteristic of this first stage of scientific thinking, established in the materialism of Democritus and his school, was not, as a matter of fact, that it built up the whole of reality from blocks of fixed matter.   Much more important was the further point that the question about the essence of the fixed matter was never raised at all.   The fixed bodies, with their inert matter and their pushing and pulling, were taken as self-explanatory original data, about which there was no further reflection.   The world was explained without remainder when men succeeded in taking it back to the motions of tiny particles.   A completely intelligible model was provided when it could be presented in the form of an interplay between the elements of rigid bodies, which rolled about

like tennis balls, so that impacts and reactions take place between them. The differing densities and weights of the
various bodies were satisfactorily explained when it was said
that in the heavier bodies the tiny corpuscles from which they
were made were more tightly packed, whereas in the lighter
ones they were dispersed more thinly; so that one could say,
with Newton, that mass is quantity of matter (*quantitas
materiae*). There was no real advance out of this simple
scientific position, characteristic of the first stage, when Newton discovered the law of gravity, and thus a third kind of
relation between the rigid elementary particles was added to
those of impact and reaction, namely action at a distance between two mutually attracting objects, in direct relation to
their mass, and in inverse relation to the square of their
distance. The goal of scientific explanation thereafter was
to explain all events, electrical, magnetic, capillary action,
osmosis, the origin and development of organic life and of
consciousness by taking them back to systems, large, small,
or microscopic, in which rigid bodies acted according to the
principle of gravitation, either circling round one another
like planets and suns, or conglomerating, or hitting one another like billiard balls. If this could be done, the world was
explained. This ideal for research, this goal of mechanical
thinking, is the clearest of all evidence for the sole sovereignty
of that technical way of thinking which the materialist faith
entails.

Once we have moved beyond this period of classical mechanics, we are for the first time able to assess what kind of crisis
was precipitated for the whole of scientific understanding,
when the question 'What is matter?' was posed irresistibly,
and soon became the central question for the whole of science.
Once this question was raised, it involved a complete transformation of previous modes of enquiry. The whole direction
in which scientific work was pressed forward was changed.
What had previously been treated as the ultimate data, to
which it was the purpose of research to refer everything else
back, had itself become the thing most questionable and in
need of explanation. What had hitherto been taken to be the
key to the solution of all the world's problems, became itself

the one great world problem, towards the solution of which generations of scientists devoted their labour. In consequence, the picture of scientific work was radically altered. Natural explanations had lost their former source of stability. The end point at which all former questions had been brought to rest had now become the starting point for new and much more radical questioning.

This transformation of physics, which Bavink called 'the liquidation of materialism', can only be exhibited in broad outline here. Modern physics stands under the sign of atomic research, that bold enterprise whereby man tries to force his way by his experiments and calculations into the secret of the fundamental particles, hidden in the womb of the atomic nucleus, a thing which today seems to us a most complicated construction though it is a thousand million times smaller than the tiniest speck. We should not forget that if an apple pip were as big as the earth, an atom would be about as big as a drop of water. If we took a billionth of a drop of water, and divided it again into a billion parts, we should have the approximate mass of the atomic nucleus. Round this nucleus, negatively charged electrons are rushing at an inconceivable rate. The nucleus itself seems to be chiefly composed of two kinds of elementary particle, according to theses current since 1932, the positively charged protons, and the electrically neutral neutrons. We cannot take it upon ourselves here to present even a rough account of the conclusions of current atomic physics. The total picture of atomic research has been transformed with uncanny speed in the last ten years, and is still in a state of flux, so that any attempt to collate the findings would be out of date very quickly. What matters to us, in this connection, is the new direction which research has taken, along which it proceeds without intermission. If we look only at the chief steps by which progress has been made, it is clear that this direction is the one followed by previous researches into the essence of matter. The starting point for further investigation was the recognition that the atom, the ultimate individual in 'granular world material', is not the rigid, inert, self-consistent mass which the older atomism had taken it to be, but a system in which even smaller elements carry out incredibly swift movements in empty space. With this discovery, motion was introduced into the dead mass of world-stuff. The discovery was as powerful, and as fraught with consequence, as the Copernican discovery that the earth was not at rest but in motion. Then came Rutherford's picture of the atom: in the middle of each atom there is a central field of force which carries a positive electrical charge. This is the nucleus. Round the nucleus move the electrons, with unimaginable velocity, and carrying a negative charge. The limits of the atom's sphere of action are fixed by a cross-section of the outermost circuit, and give a kind of shell or atmosphere up to which other atoms can approach. In the hydrogen atom, for instance, there is a nucleus with one proton, with a single electron moving round it, whereas the helium atom has two protons and two neutrons in its nucleus, and two electrons moving round it. The electric charge on the nucleus is the same as that carried by the electrons, but has the opposite sign, and the charges neutralize each other in respect of the atom's external action. The atom is electrically neutral. The fact that on earth and on the smaller stars it does not collapse is provisionally attributed to the action of a centrifugal force. The atom therefore is a tiny solar system. By far its greater part is empty space, an electric field, free of matter, in which the electrons circulate like tiny planets. In a cubic yard of lead, for instance, the amount of rigid matter is less than a pin-head. In the interior of a large fixed star, the human body would be compressed to the dimensions of a fly. Everything else is empty space. Thus one may understand why a cathode ray, which is an electron moving in a straight line at high velocity, can strike a metal sheet and generally passes through it without any change of direction, though in certain cases it may be so strongly deflected that its direction is completely reversed. This is natural enough, since most of these β-particles pass through the empty space surrounding the atomic nuclei in the metal sheet. Only if the flying electron comes near to a positive nucleus is it seriously deflected. At this first stage, then, the individual elements of which matter is composed have been transformed into solar systems subject to violent movement, but it seems possible still to treat the suns and planets of such systems as rigid little bodies, charged with positive or negative electricity as one might charge metal bullets or metal rods.   The only thing is that these charged particles, protons and electrons, are far tinier even than an electrically charged atom, a so-called ion.   But in fact both these things can be seen with the naked eye in a Wilson chamber, because, as they move, they leave behind them a trail of condensation, tiny drops of water which together form a very fine thread of cloud.   Our picture of the atom has been radically altered by all this.   It has become the scene where tremendously rapid movement is taking place. But when we attend to the fundamental particles of the tiny solar systems, it would appear that they are not fundamentally to be distinguished from the atoms of Democritus.   We still have 'absolute objects' which, as such, carry kinetic and potential energy.   It is as though in empty space there were now three kinds of entity: first, material particles which are far smaller than the atoms of which Democritus thought; secondly, energy, in the form both of kinetic energy and of fields of force, which is carried by these particles; and thirdly, subjects whose knowing faculties are directed towards these absolute objects.

The second step was taken with Max Planck's discoveries, round about 1900, which mark the beginning of a new epoch in science, and the end of an intellectual habit which, up to then, had been taken as fundamental.   Hitherto it had been believed that all transmissions of energy in the universe take place continuously; *natura non facit saltus*: nature doesn't make jumps.   To his astonishment, man discovered that energy radiated from atoms is not given off continuously, but behaves like an intermittent spring which flows in fits and starts, drop by drop perhaps, or in definite rations.   It is like the situation when a road is being repaired, and the police set up control points where the traffic accumulates for a time, and is then suddenly released.   The radiation emitted is always some multiple of a definite quantum of action, h, which is a combination of energy and time; the energy emitted being the quotient of h divided by a certain time, the time which is called in wave-theory the time of oscillation; or alternatively, the energy is the product of h and the frequency v of the emitted light. The astonishing fact is, that if we know the total energy (measured in ergs) radiated from such an intermittent source during one of the discontinuous periods of emission, and measure the characteristic time of oscillation of the energy (in seconds); if, then, we take another set of measurements, using the same source, we get a different number of ergs for the energy, and a different number of seconds for the period; but the product in erg seconds will be the same in both cases. This is true for any source of light we care to use, hydrogen, calcium, etc. This product is always h, which is $\frac{6\cdot623}{10^{27}}$ erg sec., i.e. 0·000,000,000,000,000,000,000,000,006,623 erg seconds. Even so, of course, the firm foundation of the older physics, namely its postulate that there are substantial carriers of electrical charge, has not been radically abandoned. But a new atom, an atom of action which cannot be seen or even envisaged, has come to play its part alongside the old substantial atom. To some physicists at any rate it seemed destined to crowd out the old substantial atom more and more, and to take its place as the ultimate constituent of reality.

Clearly h is itself a kind of atom, a unit bound up with the event of radiation. It is not an atom of any sort of matter, but rather an atom, or quantum, as it is usually called, of an impalpable physical magnitude of action. Whereas there are ninety-eight different kinds of material atom (or over a thousand, if you count the isotopes), there is only one quantum of action. It is always the same, in whatever relation it occurs. If, for example, a ray of light from Sirius strikes the retina in my eye, having travelled for eight years across the intervening eighty billion kilometres, and evokes the sensation of light in my eye, it can only do so inasmuch as it is composed of these h-quanta of action. This discovery was not able to demolish the old physical picture of atoms at a first assault. But it led to a revolutionary model of the atom, proposed in 1913 by the Danish physicist Niels Bohr. In this picture, the electrons which move round the nucleus are not able to do so in any arbitrary orbit. Certain paths, the quantum paths, are the only ones possible for them. It is as though tracks had been cut out for them. The second quantum path in the hydrogen atom has a diameter four times that of the first; the third is nine times that of the first; and so on. To each path belongs a distinct energy of motion. If now the atom is acted upon from outside, as for instance by the impact of a cathode ray, the electron may be thrown from the first to the second or even a higher path in a sudden quantum jump. It cannot maintain its position there for long, however, and it returns to its primary path. Energy is liberated in every such disturbance, and this energy is given off from the atom as light, or more generally as electro-magnetic radiation. Thus the atom transforms the energy of the cathode ray which strikes it. The intuitive astronomical picture of a solar system can still be retained, even at this second stage of atomic physics which is affected by Planck's discovery. The third stage, however, involves a complete reversal of the old point of view. Bohr was in difficulties with the mechanical representation from the start. For he had to allow the electron to pass from one path to another in an indemonstrable way, and thus had to postulate a jump, lacking continuity in space and time. Besides this, however, his theory, which had explained an unexpected range of otherwise incomprehensible spectroscopic facts, required to be modified in face of new observations which appeared to yield totals of action involving half h.

A succession of theoretical physicists, among them Heisenberg, Schrödinger, and Dirac, succeeded in rectifying these discrepancies. Their researches led to what is called 'the new quantum mechanics'. They were confirmed, not merely by spectroscopic observations, but, even more important, through chemistry; and they yielded a picture which could not be understood from the point of view of the Rutherford-Bohr atomic theory. Heisenberg did the most far-reaching work here. He would not allow his enquiries to be hampered by the idea that it must be generally possible to have a picture of some kind by which to conceive the atom. The material carriers of electrical energy had dissolved away. These elementary particles no longer exist as substances in solid continuity of being with an enduring self-identity; rather their existence takes place through forms where physical characteristics are not only unknown but actually undetermined, the characteristics persisting only in the recurrent determinations received through an interchange of energy with other patterns and systems. Matter has itself become energy. It is no longer the case that there is a substratum at rest, to which something happens. All that remains is the happening itself. 'The world does not be, it becomes.' We might be tempted to find here a confirmation of Genesis 1, that the whole world first arose from the creative word 'Let there be light'. This is fundamentally impossible, because the earth is already supposed to be there before this creative word is uttered, and we know today that any matter gives off energy-radiations. In the sense of the physicist, there cannot be a dark world. From the physicist's point of view, darkness means non-existence. From the point of view of the latest research, therefore, it would be premature if one were to think of the world first coming into existence with the creation of light. For already when the earth was 'waste and void', its matter was emitting radiation, unless, of course, one is prepared to maintain that it first did so only when God said 'Let there be light'. This equivalence of the world and light dates from the last stage of classical electro-dynamics, whose findings are being overhauled today. They are being admitted into the new, and still unfinished, electrodynamics of Heisenberg, only in so far as it is being established that electrons may emit and absorb enduring photons,[1] a chapter of the latest electrical theory which is still far from clear. Alongside this, however, account must be taken of Einstein's gravitational quanta, something of which at best only fleeting glimpses are available, as also that central topic in contemporary nuclear physics, the meson-fields, which are not the same as the electric fields of a charged meson (its charge being the same as that of the electron and the positron), but rather are a third thing, and therefore we come to envisage a tripartite division of cosmic forces as

[1] It is a mathematical device permissible in quantum theory which suggests this description. Whether or not this description fits the facts is not yet clear. Photons are discussed on p. 45.—(Translator's note.)

described in the affine field-theory of Einstein and Schröd-inger.[1]

One can therefore only speak of matter emerging from prior radiation of light with the proviso that not all events can be explained from electro-magnetic effects, as was believed for a long time.   Only in this restricted sense can it be said that the world consists of light, and that the creation of the world is the creation of light.   In any case, 'light' must be taken in a wider sense to cover all electro-magnetic radiation, and not merely the small range which is visible to the eye. Radiations invisible to the eye will include, for instance, those picked up by radio sets.   This brings us to the position ac-knowledged in the first sentences of the Bible, where after the opening sentences God says 'Let there be light', and 'there was light'.   Light is created before there are any heavenly lights.   All creatures which come into existence are materializations of the light which was already there when the world was originally constituted.   With this thesis, the first goal has been reached in the effort to reduce matter to energy. The invention of the atom bomb, which we do not intend to discuss in detail in this context, may serve to make this thesis clear to the world.   The principle of the atom bomb is this, that the components of the atomic nucleus, in particular the protons and neutrons, are bound together so firmly that man has tried in vain for a long time to break them apart, in order to liberate the hidden energy which accounts for their

[1] *Positrons* are comparatively rare particles, first discovered in 1932.   They are found in cosmic rays and as products of nuclear disintegration.   They have the same mass as electrons but an opposite charge.   They unite with electrons and then disappear as radiant energy.

Mesons are fundamental particles with mass intermediate between that of the electron and that of the proton.   Several different particles of this kind are now known, some with the negative charge of the electron, some with the positive charge of the positron, and some with no charge at all.   The first meson was discovered in 1936 and new types are still being found.   Most of them have a very short life-time for they decay spontaneously into mesons of lighter mass, electrons, or positrons.

Affine Field-Theory is a method of analysing the fundamental structure and physical factors of space-time, the details of which are available in E. Schrödinger: *Space-Time Structure*, Cambridge, 1950.

The three kinds of world-element in this theory are those which are or which produce three quite different fields, gravitational, electrical (Coulombic), and mesonic.   The important point is that the whole story certainly cannot be told simply in terms of classical electro-dynamics.—(Translator's note.)

adhesion in spite of the mutual repulsion of the protons. Finally, by bombarding the nucleus of the uranium atom with neutrons, collected from 'heavy water' or purest graphite, it was possible to achieve the appropriate degree of resonance. The following result was obtained by such bombardment and fission: before it was done, the atomic weight of the uranium atom was 235 units, and after the experiment it was 224 units. Where were the extra 11 units? They had been liberated in the form of energy. Here was a clear demonstration of matter being converted into energy. Everyone has an idea of the incredible supply of energy thus suddenly established out of nothing. If the technical difficulties could be overcome, a pound of uranium thus transformed into energy would produce energy equivalent to the heat generated by five million pounds of coal (over two thousand tons) or three million pounds weight of petrol. A kilogram of matter, transformed into energy, would yield twenty-five billion kilowatt-hours of work, which represents the power generated by the entire electrical supply in America during a couple of months in 1939. And, provided the technical difficulties were overcome, this could be transformed into a corresponding quantity of heat.

5. FROM LIGHT TO COMPLEMENTARITY

The efforts of the human mind to grapple with the riddle of light make up an exciting drama, in the course of which our whole picture of reality has been fundamentally changed, and philosophy too has had to work with a new situation. The course of these researches into light, from the time of Huyghens and Newton down to the present, reminds one of the exploration of a cave, where the explorers believe time after time that they have reached the end and are contemplating the whole vast gallery with its wonderland of stalactites. But every time they believe they have got to the end, they notice, almost by chance, a small crack in one of the side walls, where a man can just squeeze between two blocks of rock. When they have struggled through it, a new and yet larger hall greets their eyes, so splendid and spacious that the hall they have already traversed appears to them to be no more than the entrance hall for this more impressive underground temple. We have to sketch now the dramatic course of research into the problem of light, so far as laymen are able to follow it from a distance. For this, we may refer to the account given by Louis de Broglie, himself an important contributor to the drama, in his book *Fundamental Particles,* though it must be remembered that de Broglie has ideas of his own about light, some of which are in process of revision, and some are no longer held at all.

At first, the struggle was focused on the question: Does light consist of waves? Is the radiation of light the propagation of periodic disturbances of an invisible medium through space—the so-called aether—just as sound is the propagation of air disturbances? Or does light consist of corpuscles, or tiny grains thrown out like a hail of bullets or grape-shot from the light-source? Though Newton clung to the corpuscular theory, the wave theory ultimately triumphed through the influence of Huyghens, Young and Fresnel, early in the nineteenth century, together with the later influence of Maxwell. Two phenomena seemed to point unequivocally to the wave theory: that of refraction, where a light ray is bent, when it passes at an oblique angle from one medium to another, e.g. from air to water; and that of interference, where light is supplied through two parallel slits in a screen, and alternate light and dark fringes are observed alongside the slits, the explanation being that two sets of waves are superimposed, alternatively reinforcing and levelling out one another, so that light added to light may produce darkness. The corpuscular theory seemed to be relegated to a primitive stage, and the wave theory had won the first round of the great battle.

Then, however, came the first dramatic crisis in optical science, which, to everyone's surprise, seemed to mean that research was thrown back on the older channels despite the clear proofs in favour of the new ones. The crisis occurred because of something which at first sight seemed to be of secondary importance and hitherto hardly worthy of notice, like the small crack in the cave wall which the explorers did not see at first, but which called all existing theories into question. This was the so-called photo-electric effect. What does this phrase mean? Every unit of matter contains within itself electrically charged particles, electrons, which at normal temperatures cannot be detached from it. If the bit of matter is exposed to an appropriate source of energy, however, it is possible that electrons may be ejected from it. Experiments showed that when the matter is at a great distance from the light-source, electrons are still detached, provided that the frequency of the light is high enough. (Frequency is measured by the number of wave-crests passing a given point in one second.) Naturally the number of electrons ejected in a second diminishes as the distance is increased between the light-source and the exposed material. But some ejections happen, however great the distance.

Light, therefore, however small its intensity may be, can always produce this photo-electric effect, provided its frequency does not fall below a certain number. From this fact it is possible to conclude whether light consists of waves, or whether it has a granular structure. Think of a source of light placed opposite a screen which is therefore exposed to it at a given distance. Whether light has wave-formation, or whether it consists of particles, the light-energy received at the screen will be the same for that given distance. But the radiated light-energy will have a different distribution on the screen in one case from what it has in the other. If light has a wave-formation, it will radiate towards the screen by a rolling wave-front which is the same at all points, so that all parts of the screen will receive light-energy during the whole period of radiation. All parts of the screen will have received the same tiny amount of light. But if the light consists in corpuscles, the radiation can be compared to the intermittent fire of a machine-gun throwing out little bullets on all sides, and the particular points of the screen which happen to be hit will receive a relatively large amount of light, whereas other points which are not hit will receive none at all. Now let us suppose that there is a bit of mechanism used in radiation experiments which operates only when it is affected by a certain amount of energy which must be above a fixed minimum. Think, if you like, of a clock which is wound up, but which needs a certain touch to the pendulum to set it going. This bit of mechanism is in fact a parable of the electron, which requires a particular shock before it is thrown out of the bit of matter and produces the photo-electric effect. If light is a wave which spreads equally through space, then its power to produce effects would become uniformly weaker the further the ray has travelled from its source. Therefore, if the mechanism needs a shock of some fixed intensity in order to make it work, a point will be reached where the process will never be set in motion at all, since the bit of matter will be so far from the light-source that the wave which reaches it is too weak to do the job. The case is completely different if the light is not a wave but consists of corporeal light-grains. The danger of the mechanism being hit by one of the bullets, to put it pictorially, is much less if its distance from the machine gun is very great. The hail of bullets is not so thick at a considerable distance from the machine gun as it is a few yards from its nozzle. But even at a considerable distance from the gun, the danger has not vanished completely. For if firing goes on long enough, or, to put it directly, if exposure to the light is for a sufficiently long period, it is always possible that a bullet will find its mark, that the mechanism will be hit by a stray shot, and thereby be set in motion. We see, therefore, that if it can be shown that at great distances from the source of light there is always a possibility of the photo-electric effect, which requires a definite amount of energy, then it is proved that light is not a wave-front but a hail of bullets. Whatever arguments there may be to the contrary, it clearly must have a corpuscular character, not a wave-formation. This was the second act of the exciting drama in which man grappled with the problem of light in order to uncover its secret. The corpuscular theory has won the second round. The victory found its expression in that Planck proceeded to evaluate the elementary quantum h, and Einstein carried the matter a stage further by showing that light, with frequency v, consists of energy-corpuscles equal to hv. These energy corpuscles, which became important elements in the theory of light, were called light-quanta, or more generally *photons*.

If the investigation of light had stopped at this point, it would not have led to a revolution in the complete world-picture. The old world-picture would simply have been re-adopted. One would have turned back to the old representation of light particles as Newton knew it. The classical view which presented light as made up of tiny grains flying through space on their appointed paths, and thus similar in constitution to the rest of the material world, would in fact have won an all-round victory over the wave picture. But this simple return to what obtained before the advent of the wave theory was no longer possible. The way back was blocked. The insurmountable obstacle which nothing can eliminate from the world was the event called interference, and this, as we saw earlier, can only be explained from the wave character of light. An attempt was made to elucidate the phenomenon of interference by saying that a number of corpuscles could come together and counteract one another. But this corpuscular explanation of interference failed. For the interference fringes still appeared on photographic plates after a sufficiently long exposure, when no more than a single photon, not a number of them, was available at the same instant to the interference apparatus. Any reciprocal action within the group of corpuscles was thus ruled out from the start. The photons were not able to reach the apparatus in simultaneous groups, but only one by one.

And thus the drama of man's struggle to work out the secret of light reached its climax. It had issued in a tragic conflict. Nature seemed to contradict itself. Two insuperable facts with which Nature confronts us seemed incapable of reconciliation. On the one side were the interference fringes, where waves reinforced or cancelled out one another. This was comprehensible if light were a wave, that is to say a homogeneous structure spreading through space. On the other side were certain effects, impossible to deny, chief among them the photo-electric effect. These could not be evoked by a wave but only by a particle, and therefore by something which has a point-structure and thus is confined to a very limited space. Could there be any resolution of this dramatic tension, this tragic conflict?

A solution is possible only if we are prepared to give up the basic presupposition with which man has approached reality from the very beginning of scientific investigation, and which for centuries has been accepted as self-evident; namely, the assumption that the world, whose secrets we hope to unravel by our experiments, is an objective world of things. If we have to do with a world of things, in which things pursue their course through space out there beyond ourselves, then an object which moves here in front of our eyes can only at that moment be either a moving corpuscle, with a particular location in space and·a particular speed, or a wave which is spread out through the whole of space. The situation will be different only if, from the outset, we are not dealing with an 'absolute object' there over against us, but rather that we have observing subject involved in the whole event. If that is the case, then we should give up the hypothesis that at a given moment the corpuscle is at a particular point in space and is moving along a certain track with a certain velocity. The corpuscle is only at a particular point when it betrays its presence at that point to an observing or experimenting subject by some specific effect. At once, therefore, the two notions of light waves and light particles take on a new sense in which they can be reconciled. The light wave is no longer a wave which we are able to conceive as a purely objective event, like for instance a sound wave which occurs as the air is alternately thinned and thickened, or like a wave on the sea which propagates over a wide area an initial disturbance of the water. We now have a wave which can only be described if we include an observing subject in the description from the very start. It is a wave, therefore, in which no absolute objective event takes place independently of an observing subject. It is, in fact, the wave which expresses *the variation in the probability* of a corpuscle betraying its presence by some specific effect to an observing subject at any point in space. Let us try to offer an illustration by way of explanation of this so-called 'probability-wave'. Suppose that on a warm summer evening the lights are on in a dance hall, and the windows are wide open. Moths fly into the room steadily through the windows, and dance round the chandelier which hangs in the centre. The moths in fact are fluttering all over the room, and no one can be sure where they will find a moth at any moment. But the probability of finding the moth in question is greatest in the neighbourhood of the chandelier. Now suppose that the chandelier is set in motion, and swings gently to and fro with periodic motion, then the probability of pointing out a given moth at a particular point increases and decreases with the motion of light. And now try to think the chandelier and its flames completely out of the picture, for while it is there it makes the whole business explicable in mechanical terms since the flames attract the moths. Attend simply to the possibility which you anticipate, first at one point, and then at another, of being brushed by a flying moth; and that gives some kind of illustration of a probability-wave. It is clear from the outset that some subject or other must be in the picture, to whom the moth betrays its presence by brushing against him, and to whom that experience is more or less probable. Now, therefore, we can say with de Broglie: 'The photon is associated with a light wave.' This light wave determines the probability with which the photon may be observed by me, an observer, at this point in space where I stand, by reason of some observable effect, e.g. a photo-electric effect. If the wave has a high intensity, then there is a high probability that the photon will betray its presence through an observable effect. Where the associated wave is of only small amplitude, the prospect is correspondingly small. This is particularly clear when we take a photograph in very weak light. When the light is so weak that the photons pass through the interference apparatus singly, one after another, one is still able to record light fringes, caused by interference, as seemed probable and indeed predictable on the wave-theory, despite the fact that each single photon produces a localized effect on the photographic plate. It can therefore be said that 'the photon is potentially present in the wave'. To indicate this potential presence we can introduce an expression used in the previous section and say: 'The photon is not yet objectified, and thus it has not yet made an objective appearance at a given point.' We can therefore understand how de Broglie is able to say: 'As soon as the localized effect of the proton makes its appearance, the potential presence of the proton in the wave vanishes, and the wave itself is extinguished. The wave-aspect of the proton vanishes when it shows its corpuscular aspect by its localization.' The two aspects belong necessarily together, and yet they mutually limit one another. All these modes of expression used by contemporary physicists have meaning obviously only when the description of natural events contains a reference to an observing subject who is himself included in the event. • For an absolute object, existing over and above any awareness, cannot be 'extinguished'. An objective entity cannot collapse into nothingness from moment to moment.

The drama of man's struggle to unravel the secret of light has thus reached the final act. In this last act, a synthesis is achieved between the two contradictory pictures by means of which the essence of light is portrayed in virtue of the experiments made. The Either/Or of corpuscle and wave, particle and field, discontinuous given-ness and continuity, is thus removed and resolved in a higher unity. The two pictures, mutually exclusive, presented us with an insoluble contradiction so long as we approached reality with the outlook of the classical theory of knowledge, assuming that we were dealing with a reality over against consciousness. But as soon as this outlook is abandoned, the contradiction is transformed into a relation of 'complementarity' between two diverse aspects in which reality manifests itself, according as the observing subject, without whom reality cannot be completely described, encounters it by means of his observations and his measuring instruments.

The fact that one speaks in contemporary physics, particularly in popular expositions where the mathematical apparatus is neglected, about a 'dualism' obtaining between two 'sides' or 'aspects', tempts us to suppose all too easily that the secret of the complementarity of two mutually contradictory pictures can be explained to some extent by thinking of the everyday fact, which we all accept with complete confidence in three-dimensional space, that a body, say a statue, can be studied or photographed from many sides, from the front or back, or in profile.

These different aspects of any body can all be unified with one another without contradiction even within the old realistic world-picture. That a house or a human body can be simultaneously looked at from many sides has by no means upset the old notion of objectivity, and we take it for granted that all physical structures can similarly be looked at from many sides at once within three-dimensional space. The pictures afforded of them can always be combined. But here, the incomprehensible thing which upsets the whole world of classical objectivity, is that one and the same reality appears under two forms which can never be held together within corporeal space as we envisage it, and which, occurring simultaneously as they do, seem to cancel each other out. While this is a possibility, even in only one corner of the world of experience, it means the collapse of that whole structure of objectivity within which the human mind has become domesticated for centuries. The dualism of corpuscle and wave pictures, when thought out carefully, carries with it a complete transformation of the classical notion of reality. It leads to the demolition of its very foundation stones. Within research into physics itself, this has already been demonstrated, in that the new knowledge obtained by research into the problem of light cannot be confined to this restricted field. The discoveries extend far beyond the boundaries of Optics. One cannot escape the thought that what is true of light-quanta may also be true of the other fundamental particles of which matter consists. It has already been shown that Planck's quantum of action has to be introduced into the mechanics of the fundamental particles within the atom, if we are to understand the motions of the electrons. These motions of the electrons also must be associated with waves. The elements of matter, as they are displayed in Bohr's model of the atom, always make themselves known only by localized intermittent effects. In the intervals, it is impossible to ascribe to them at any moment a place in space. The intensity of the wave associated with a particle gives the probability, for an electron as well as for a photon, that the particle will betray its presence at a given point by some effect.

We do not intend, in this context, to follow out further the philosophical consequences of this. Here our concern is simply with the significance for a world-view of this wave-corpuscle complementarity. To grasp this, it is sufficient to have traced the findings of modern physics up to the point where quantum mechanics spills over from the field of Optics, and its application is extended beyond photons to the fundamental particles of matter, with the result that one comes to entertain the bold idea, impossible within classical physics, that the electron may be understood just as well in terms of a wave as of a particle, which is something confirmed at once by experiment.

6. FROM PHYSICS TO PHILOSOPHY

Physics, by its own results, has been brought to a critical juncture at this point. Either it must rest content with an insoluble riddle, or it must venture out of its own territory and undertake to dismantle the foundations upon which the whole of our Western thinking has hitherto been built. By doing so, it trespasses upon the field of philosophy. With very few exceptions our younger physicists are of the opinion that the dualism of corpuscle and wave, particle and field, presents us not merely with a problem in physics which could be solved by experiments and calculations, but rather with an ultimate philosophical problem. It seems as though our thinking had gone astray inside a labyrinth, and we can see no way out. Faced with the ultimate epistemological problems which confront us here, physical research has emerged from its isolation, and must now be seen in a wider context. This point of view is one which has been expressed in a whole series of publications by contemporary physicists. To find a way out of the labyrinth, C. F. von Weizsäcker[1] has turned back to Kant's Transcendental Aesthetic. The thing-in-itself lies on the further side of the entire world of appearances. It is an

[1] Two books by von Weizsäcker are now available in English: *The History of Nature*, and *The World View of Physics*.

unknown x standing outside all forms of intuition.[1] Only on such terms are we able to understand how it can be presented to us in two quite different modes which produce an antinomy. The antinomy occurs only within our phenomenal world, not within the unobservable reality itself. In his preface to de Broglie's book on fundamental particles, von Weizsäcker tries to relate the physical law of complementarity to a higher and more general law which extends throughout the physical realm, and includes also within its range the realm of the soul or the 'spiritual'. He says that 'this is perhaps only a special case of a universal state of affairs. The extension of a coloured surface in space, the flux of a motion in time, and the stream of our thoughts and feelings, are all continuous so long as we do not mark off any individual moment. But every act of attention is discrete and indivisible, and creates discontinuity. It may be that the law of continuity and discontinuity in our experience is everywhere connected with the difference between events occurring and experimental grasp of them.'

While von Weizsäcker tries to solve this ultimate physical problem by reference to Kant's theory of knowledge, Jordan finds a starting point for his attempted philosophical solution in the positivist philosophy developed by Richard Avenarius and Ernst Mach in the post-Kantian epoch as the final outcome of radical empiricism. In *Verdrängung und Komplementarität (Displacement and Complementarity)*, he establishes a connection between atomic research and modern psychology. Freud's theory of the unconscious offers a striking parallel to the complementarity of wave and corpuscle, and to Heisenberg's 'uncertainty-principle'. According to Heisenberg, we can specify precisely where a moving electron is, or the momentum of its motion (mass × velocity), but never both at

---

[1] The terms *Anschauung, anschaulich*, etc., are difficult to translate. Following the normal usage in translations of Kant, they have generally been translated by 'intuition', etc., in this book. No more is intended by this term than some direct or immediate mode of knowledge. Sometimes (as in III, 10 and 11) the translator has adopted the suggestion made in von Weizsäcker's *The World View of Physics*, p. 13, and has used words like 'perceptibility' or 'envisaging'. Von Weizsäcker associates the quality of *Anschaulichkeit* with the theories of classical physics, because they describe nature by models formed by analogy with things perceived by the senses. A most important feature of quantum-mechanics is that its terms of description transcend all suggestion of 'perceptibility'.—(Translator's note.)

once. If its location is precisely determined, its momentum is relegated to the realm of the unobservable, and vice versa. This kind of mutually exclusive disjunction (Either/Or) is also the case, according to Freud, in instances of dual consciousness or dual personality, where the same body is controlled by two different 'persons'. Here also only one person can be dominant at any one time, the form in which the other is experienced being that of abnormal intrusion from some other dimension. An example would be the fact that some mediums enjoy striking artistic powers in a state of trance. The fact that it is impossible to specify both location and momentum at the same time, or simultaneously to objectify both the wave picture and the corpuscle picture, has obvious affinity with the law by which two persons, or two fragments of personality, cannot at the same time control a body. One of them must always relegate the other to 'the Unconscious'.

By means of this striking parallel, the law of complementarity has been extended to cover the whole field of atomic physics and has been given a much broader basis which exhibits its universal significance and its relevance to the whole of nature and of thought. But the use made of this parallel is not yet sufficient to make the fundamental law really comprehensible from all possible aspects. In the preface to his book *Physikalisches Denken in der neuen Zeit* (*Recent Physical Thought*), Pascual Jordan says that the philosophical basis which physicists are looking for today has now for the first time acquired the character of a necessary aid to their own work, because they have here been left in the lurch by professional philosophy. 'The physicists, therefore, have had to produce for themselves their own epistemological equipment to meet the requirements of their work, and they have done this with a determination whose radicalism has provoked the opposition of many philosophers.'

The fact that this self-made epistemological equipment is not yet good enough, and that the positivism of the more recent physics does not solve all the problems which thinking men raise in this connection, is most obvious at one particular point. The thoughtful layman is baffled by the Heisenberg Uncertainty Principle because inevitably he comes to see the matter like this. It is obvious enough that we cannot determine the location of a moving electron in the microphysical world without 'taking a sight' of it, and thereby deflecting it from its path. The procedure of surveying it therefore inevitably affects the object whose location we are trying to determine. Every microphysical process of observation involves some interference with what is observed. The layman therefore cannot help wondering why it is not possible, at least in principle, to take into account from the beginning the deflection of the object from its original path by reason of its being observed, much as a sportsman does when he takes aim at a flying bird. But this possibility must be ruled out completely. For in the field of elementary processes there is no method of observation which allows of any prior calculation of the disturbance effected in what is being observed. Here the observer cannot take aim in the same way as does the sportsman, or the anti-aircraft gunner. Such a possibility could only be envisaged by someone who was still in the toils of the classical notion of reality. An evaluation of the situation in the sense of classical physics has become demonstrably untenable. Philipp Lennard, under the patronage of the political authorities in the Third Reich, tried to produce such an evaluation with considerable skill, but without success. The facts as now understood amount to this, that the new and successful theoretical conjectures demand a new epistemology.

What, then, is the new point of departure from which contemporary physics approaches the experimental results? Pascual Jordan, in agreement with Ernst Mach, sums it up in the word positivism. But what is meant by this word whose meanings are so varied? The modern scientist, says Jordan, no longer seeks to penetrate with understanding to the interior of nature, as did the medieval alchemists with their mystical scientific passion (compare, for instance, Goethe's Faust); nor does he seek to pass by way of inferences from the world of appearances to the mysterious reality, the thing in itself, hidden behind the veil of the visible world; nor does he want to explain natural processes in the terms used by classical physics of Newton's time, where explanation meant a reduction of natural processes to a mechanical model, a model of large, small, or infinitesimal solar systems where bodies moved in accordance with the laws of impact and gravitation. Modern positivist natural science has turned its back on this kind of understanding and explanation, and has done so explicitly, decisively and soberly. It no longer wants to understand but only to describe. The object of science is simply the collection and arrangement and recording of direct observations and experiences. The experimental facts themselves are the sole substance of natural science; its goal is attained and it celebrates its greatest triumph when, as in the case of Maxwell's work on electricity, it is able on the basis of previous experiments to predict accurately and successfully the result of future experiments. (*Op. cit.*, pp. 34ff.) Nowhere in modern scientific literature can we find a more clear and simple statement of the goal which attracts the younger generation of physicists. For that very reason, we who are not natural scientists are able at this point to make it clear why this philosophical basis of modern physics appears to us to be no more than a fruitful starting point, which has not been thought through to the end and which still requires amplification. Philosophical discussion of positivism, even in the days of Avenarius and Mach, brought out the point that the notion of positivism meant something clearly definable only from a negative point of view, namely the renunciation of every explanation of natural phenomena, and a denial of meaning to the whole question of what lies beyond our experience. When we have carried through this radical negation and completely cast aside, put out of mind, and divorced ourselves from, everything which lies beyond the content of experience and cannot be directly observed, we have to face the great question: What is left? What is the positive thing that we still have in our hands as the content of experience? To avoid answering this question, Avenarius, in his principal work *Kritik der reinen Erfahrung* (*Critique of Pure Experience*), expressed this pure content by letters such as are used in mathematics to denote numerical values related by certain functions, rather than by using words or ideas; e.g. C, C^1, C^2, . . . c, c^1, c^2. . . . Pascual Jordan does not do this. In his chapter on ' physical positivism ' he speaks quite clearly about 'observations', 'experiences', 'laboratory events', which cannot be further clarified or understood, but which can nevertheless be described. If, however, in the course of this description, we are determined to rule out all reference to what is objective, in the classical sense of the term, and also all 'metaphysical hinterworlds', then it is clear 'that in the pure description of the positive thing which survives by this method, we can indeed eliminate the "object", in the old sense of the word; but one thing belongs necessarily to the description, even when we are really only describing, and in no sense wanting to explain or understand'. This is the subject, which observes, experiences, experiments in the laboratory, and therefore is able to describe. Apart from this postulate, the words observation, experience and event lose all meaning. An observer observing is not, indeed, a matter of objective experience.[1] But neither is he a metaphysical phantom which we have deliberately constructed. He is, as Rickert says, a datum who is in direct proximity to us and in whom we trust. He is better trusted and better known than is the entire objective world which stands over against us. This subject, therefore, belongs necessarily within the state of affairs we are describing, but which we cannot further explain or understand. When we leave out the subject, we have not given a complete description of the state of affairs. We have made an abstraction from what is necessarily always the case.

Let us therefore examine the matter from the point of view of the self, which is now given as the one fundamental datum, and try to clarify the situation created for physical research now that atomic research has led up to this point where the experimental investigation of fundamental particles involves a dualism of two aspects which cannot be brought into harmony: particle and field, corpuscle and wave. We will state the matter as simply as possible.

We can hardly help representing the human eye, whose retina receives light waves sent out from an object, as a mirror in which is reflected the absolute object which stands in front of it. For the sake of having a concrete example, suppose we

---

[1] See the previous volume: *Christian Faith and Natural Science.*

have the Great Pyramid in front of us among the desert sands, and we work out how this pyramid evokes a reflection in the eyes of a man who is looking at it. Something happens which is as remarkable as we should find it to be if, instead of the reflection we expect in a mirror turned towards the pyramid, first a sphere, and then a cylinder, were to appear as if by magic. This double effect does not come about through any alteration in the reflection itself, but through a change in method which produces the complementarity. Light, geometrically speaking, whether received by some optical (reflecting) apparatus, or on the retina, or on a photographic plate, exhibits a wave character; it does so in the phenomenon of refraction too, and therefore apart from all the special phenomena of interference. But if light be regarded from the point of view of energy, with the help of a photo-electric cell and an electron conductor (Geiger counter), it exhibits a photon character. This abnormal situation presents us with two possibilities in an Either/Or relation. Either, the reality in which we find ourselves, and to which we belong, contains an insoluble contradiction at the heart of the tiny fundamental constituents of which it is composed, for, we are unable to see these two pictures together with the powers of knowledge we possess. In this case, it would seem, our research loses all meaning. Or, and this is the other possibility which alone remains open, we are driven to the conclusion that the representation of reality with which we started is a false one, namely the notion that reality, to put it figuratively, stands as an absolute object over against our consciousness, and evokes a reflection of its being in our consciousness. Clearly this notion has to be abandoned, and we must simply acknowledge what we really see, without prejudice and without any dogmatic interpretation. In strict truth we do not see the supposed object. What we see is merely the content of a perception, which we can only suppose (and never prove) to be a reflection expressing something objective. When in sober modesty this has become quite clear to us, we shall be in the position which physics sees itself to be in today.

A physical phenomenon such as an electron or a proton, whether it has the form of a particle or the character of a wave, is never there for itself alone, as pure object; rather it is always the case that an observer is there as well, directing his measuring instruments upon it. The unknown x which confronts us in this event is only evoked in this particular form through the act of observation. It is merely there when we 'call it on to the stage' by the project of making an observation. As Arthur March says in his book *Natur und Erkenntnis* (*Nature and Knowledge*), p. 213: 'The world is not separable from an observing subject.' Neils Bohr was once of the opinion that the circular motions of the electrons which he propounded had an objective significance. But a consistent picture was possible only when wave-mechanics substituted for the idea of an objective electron path that of a non-homogeneous thick cloud, which no longer related to the atom in itself, but rather to the content of our observations of the atom.

To avoid any misunderstanding, it is necessary to insert a parenthesis here. The thesis that the world is inseparable from an observer suggests to the naïve mind an immediate objection. Suppose a man is looking at the full moon, whose rays strike his eyes, then it is perfectly easy to distinguish clearly between the full moon itself, and the man whose eyes are turned towards the sky. The two are separable from one another: the full moon up in heaven, which was already shining before any man lived down here on earth, and the man on earth. This objection is rooted in a confusion. We confuse the two quite different meanings which the terms 'self' or 'observing subject' can bear. In everyday life we mean by the word 'I' our human body. This, with all the organs belonging to it, is part of the objective world, and stands in contrast to the bodies of other men with whom we live. Obviously the earth can be thought of as without men. Palaeontology describes the earth as it appeared before the first men lived on it. But we mean something quite different by the words 'I' or 'subject' in a philosophical context, where we use them to speak of the non-objective self, which sits there in the darkened stalls, itself incapable of being objectified, but confronting the whole of objective reality including the human body and also the whole world of the human drama with its suppressed complexes, and letting the whole objective world of experience pass before it in the perspective afforded by its particular seat.   When the physicist says that the world is inseparable from the observing subject, he can only mean this non-objective self, which, however, is localized in a body. Whether it is the earth itself, or an electron, which passes before me, an observing subject always belongs to the objective picture.   This indeed has the same necessity as the spatial form with a fixed number of dimensions within which any picture of the physical world must be cast.   The observing subject belongs ineradicably and at every moment to the observed object as alone it is given and with which alone we are dealing in an experiment; so that it is a wrong question to ask, if you want to know what is happening to the particle during the time it is not being observed, where it is, or what motions it is carrying out.   Nothing at all can be said about this.   Any answer we give to a wrong question is bound to be false.

Those who have not previously encountered these latest findings of contemporary physics find them too unfamiliar to be comfortable with them.   For they are in profound contrast to all our accustomed modes of thought, and we incline to think that they are the product of some high-flown human speculations which have lost contact with the solid ground of reality and of healthy human understanding, and for that reason contradict everything we expect or postulate on the basis of our own convictions.   But the opposite is the case. Here it is not a matter of precarious constructions, but rather of acknowledgments which physicists have been compelled to make against their wills, in conflict with their own assumptions and preconceptions, because of the experimental facts. Nevertheless, they do not expect us to give up our former relation to reality simply on their authority or on the reports of their experiments, and plunge into the tremendous revolution affecting the very foundations of our thinking which is at stake here.   Such a transformation, which will affect all areas once it has begun, cannot be achieved at a single blow.   Only very gradually can we adjust ourselves to it.   Further, there are physicists who are still trying to interpret the things which obtrude themselves upon us so inevitably here within the framework of the old notion of objectivity. But then we have to reckon with the astonishing fact, to which we must return in another context, that all measurements within the boundaries of the action-quantum h are unmanageable. The physicist puts the situation like this. Planck's constant h creates a gulf between us, the subjects, and the objective reality to which we must firmly adhere, and the gulf cannot be bridged. This gulf makes objective reality inaccessible to the physicist. If light be taken as an example, we have to say that light as such, the absolute object which confronts us here, is something we cannot observe at all. All that can be observed are the effects it produces on the atoms of the retina, or of a photographic plate, or of a photo-electric cell. Therefore the nature of light must be inferred from these effects. It would only be possible to do this if the interaction of light with matter took place in so determinate a fashion that a simple and irreversible relation obtained between source and effect. But here again we have reached the limits set to our observations by the constant h. This limit makes it impossible, once for all, to observe how the light operates in order to produce an effect in the atom. We can trace the course of the light ray, from its source to the moment when it enters the atom. We can observe the state of affairs which intervenes between the emission of the light ray and its arrival at the atom; and then we can observe that an effect has occurred in the atom. But the occurrence itself is not susceptible to observation. As March puts it, it is as though the constant h puts a grid over nature whose points are at a distance h from each other, and whenever nature is about to be subjected to measurement it is required to jump from one grid point to another. As we saw at an earlier stage, the electrons in Bohr's model of the atom can only move in specified orbits, and, under given influences, must always move by the so-called quantum-jump out of one orbit into the next highest one. But it is impossible to observe the quantum-jump itself, and this jump does not yield to demonstrative analysis.

When we read descriptions of this kind in contemporary

physics, we still see 'Nature' before us as an absolute object, resembling the veiled picture of Sais in Schiller's poem. The curtain which conceals it from the youth who thirsts for knowledge does not entirely cover it. There are chinks through which we catch glimpses of the picture, if only for a moment. But there is a mischievous goblin there as well, playing hide and seek with us. For the moment the youth's curiosity is roused by a fleeting glimpse through a chink in the curtain, the goblin pulls it together again like a flash, just at the point when things had become specially interesting.

All these illustrations of the puzzling state of affairs we meet at this point can naturally only be taken as parables, by whose help the physicist constantly tries to hold on, as far as possible, to the traditional point of view that nature stands over against the observing subject in complete independence; something which is always there whether we observe it or not.

The new thing we know about nature, since Planck's discovery of the h-constant, does not, according to these descriptions, consist in the fact that nature itself behaves differently from what we had hitherto believed. The new discovery relates to the accessibility of objective nature, or the possibility of control, with respect to our human powers of knowledge. It relates to the possibility of saying something about what is happening in nature as an objective world; to the capacity of men with their sense organs and measuring instruments to penetrate to the essence of the world. From this point of view, it is thought, the new physics is to be contrasted with classical physics, where it was possible to dream of Laplace's all-knowing mind, in that it has erected insuperable barriers for men, and reduced us to a condition of humbled modesty, where we can no longer explain, but only describe; so that nature remains for us a book with seven seals.

This statement of the case does not do justice to the stage to which research has now been carried, but still represents a state of transition where the ultimate goal towards which the whole development tends has not yet been reached. This goal is achieved, and the crucial turn has been taken by which our whole relation to reality is fundamentally altered, when the liberating recognition comes upon us that 'the world is not separable from an observing subject'.[1]

It is then no longer the case that nature plays a puzzling game of hide-and-seek with us, concealing itself from us so that we cannot see where a particular natural object is and what movements it is carrying out. The object, in the old sense, simply is not there. It has no place; it cannot be localized; it cannot be objectified at all. For its being is not to be separated from the observing subject which summons it on to the lighted stage of the objective world by the act of observation. From these perspectives, the conflict set up by the same object appearing from one side in the image of a particle, and from another side in the image of a wave, disappears without any remainder, when it has been made clear once for all that to every panorama which appears before us there belongs a subject which is not separable from the object. An object can never have a particular form independently of the self with its organs and instruments of observation. It has its form together with a particular subject in a particular moment. Another subject may take the place of this one, perhaps by an instance of the law of displacement where I am displaced by another 'I', or perhaps by a different instance of the law, which also governs my passage through time, where I remain the same self, existing however in a new moment which displaces the other moment, so that my observation takes place in a new context, possibly by a new arrangement of the experiment. If so, an entirely new panorama comes automatically into effect. This mysterious, but inescapable, mutual conditioning of subject and object does not consist in the fact that subject and object co-operate in the production of a panorama like two sources which collaborate to produce an effect, as, for instance, in the growth of a plant there is a contribution from beneath the earth on one side, and from sun and rain on the other. Subject and object are not causal coefficients of a natural process in this manner, so that it is possible to distinguish which part of the total effect is contributed by one party, and which by the other. It would then be possible to hold them apart as warp and weft in a

---

[1] March, *op. cit.*, p. 213.

piece of weaving. With subject and object this is totally impossible. From beginning to end, both are inseparably there, and each conditions the other. Matters being thus, there can be no contradiction when two aspects are observed which cannot be combined within one view. The two panoramas displace one another in turn, so that the elements in each view never come into conflict. That nevertheless they are strangely related in a unity, can be seen by means of a completely non-pictorial, purely abstract mathematical equation, which expresses the relation of the two complementary aspects. In this equation we grasp a non-pictorial equivalence which makes manifest an order which we cannot envisage but which we can think. We surmise that there is a mind behind everything, which still holds sway at the point where human conception reaches its limits.

With this last development of the physical world-picture, where it changes into a philosophical one, religious faith in matter, the last faith which man has created for himself, is completely demolished. Let us look back over the road which has led to this goal. First, matter, which had been believed to be eternal, dissolved itself into forms of energy comparable with light. This was the first stage of the process which prepared for the great change. Then came the drama of man's struggle with the puzzle about light. In the course of this struggle, research suggested two incompatible pictures, corpuscle and wave, particle and field. This baffling dual conclusion of research into the nature of light seemed to threaten the security of the entire physical method of research. The human mind appeared to have moved into a cul-de-sac from which there was no obvious way out. The only salvation was to admit that there is a flaw in the epistemological grounds of natural investigation. This flaw lay in the separation of the object of investigation from the investigating subject. Incontrovertible experimental facts and the reflections to which they gave rise, and not arbitrary epistemological speculation, compelled those engaged in physical research to include the subject from the very outset within the total picture of the atomic world. And thus the ultimate component of the reality with which we have to deal came to be no longer something dead, opposite to our mind and alien to it, but something psychical and alive; something analogous, however remotely, to what in the human sphere we call a self. It is not incumbent upon us to say any more about this psychical entity which we meet in the infinitesimal region. In a chapter about universal animation in the previous philosophical volume,[1] it was said that though the signs of soul-life which we meet everywhere in nature seem to us strange and incomprehensible, because they seem to have little similarity to our human consciousness, this by no means implies that the consciousness, upon whose remote tracks we seem to stumble, happens at a deeper level than that of our own inner life. Here also we are obliged to say with the utmost modesty, that what we are dealing with in physics is different from our soul-life. It is possible that there are immeasurably wider and richer realms of consciousness, to which men like ourselves can have no access through lack of experience, but which are not impoverished compared with our own, and may perhaps be richer. But whether or not this world of consciousness which is foreign to us is richer than ours, one thing is clear. If in general it has some kind of analogy, however faint, to our own psychic world, then it must in any case have one thing in common with us. The self-life, of which here we catch a gleam, is set within the world of experience at a particular place. The fact that we confront the manifestations of it without full comprehension is an expression of the inexorable law of displacement as it applies to an exclusive Either/Or, and this separates us from it, and destroys every possible bridge for the understanding. But wherever we have an instance of something providentially set at a particular place within this world, in whatever form, a question hangs over it, amounting perhaps to no more than a muffled longing, but present to all forms of conscious life: 'Whence do I come, and where am I going?' What has thrown me into the infinite cosmos at this precise place, and given me this irrevocable rôle to sustain? Even where this question comes to the surface only as muted longing, there are only the two possible answers to it which we know explicitly. Either we

[1] Cf. *Christian Faith and Natural Science*, pp. 102, 108.

have been brought forth out of nothing and are returning to nothing. Or there is a power standing over all beings, which has set each of us at our particular place, in order to draw us unto itself, when alone we shall find rest. It is significant that already in the Old Testament the inorganic world, matter so-called, does not appear as a dead object, but is summoned to rejoice in God, to engage in prayer to God and praise to the Creator. 'The heights of the mountains are his also' (Ps. 95.4); 'Let the hills sing for joy together' (Ps. 98.8; 'Mountains and all hills, praise ye the Lord' (Ps. 148.9).

III

FAITH IN ABSOLUTE TIME AND ABSOLUTE SPACE AND ITS DISRUPTION BY THE THEORY OF RELATIVITY

7. CALCULATION IN TERMS OF A FIXED WORLD-CENTRE AS A RELIGIOUS FAITH

Human reflection in terms of the absolute object, which has provisionally come to an end in the notion of the complementarity of two world-aspects, had its origin, as we saw in the last section, in the faith in the eternity of matter held by Democritus and Leucippus. We also saw that this ancient Greek faith was not merely the fruit of some primitive picture of nature, but at the same time an expression of a profound religious need for something stable 'which man must have', something indestructible to which he can commit himself unconditionally. From the biblical point of view, the long process by which this firm ground of an absolute object was chipped away, bit by bit, from under man's feet, till in the end he was left with no such ground to stand on, was a gracious catastrophe, in the course of which the divinizing of matter was exposed as a lost human cause, and man was left with only two possibilities. Either he could abandon himself unsupported to the Void, which is Nihilism, or he could throw himself for better or worse into the arms of the invisible and incomprehensible Creator. But for the human mind to come to such a frontier-situation as the Bible indicates, it is necessary, as we have demonstrated, that the ultimate hypotheses of philosophical theory should be caught up in a disturbance which has the proportions of an earthquake.

The second absolute, which stands alongside the absolute object as an obstacle in the way of complete trust in God alone, is absolute space and absolute time, or, more precisely, a system of co-ordinates embracing absolute space and absolute time, whose origin is the middle of the cosmos, and by reference to which man orientates himself in all his spatial and temporal measurements. This absolute also is not merely the expression of a primitive picture of nature, in which a plate-like earth is the 'theatre of world history' and the centre of the cosmos.

Faith in a fixed centre of the world is the expression of a profound religious need, far more so indeed than is the ancient Greek faith of Democritus in the eternal and unchangeable atom. Not only must man have 'something constant'. He also wants to be safe. He wants to be at home in a 'container' resting on eternal foundations, inside which all things have their place. The decisive thing about the religious need which is now in question is not that the earth as such is a fixed centre. Another star could take that place equally well. What is crucial is that the universe as a whole should have a centre at rest, to which all measurements may be referred. This is demonstrated by an acknowledged fact.

The Church, after a long struggle it is true, found itself able to take up a positive attitude to the world-picture of Copernicus, Kepler, and Galileo. These astronomers had indeed deprived the earth of its position as the central body, but, as Copernicus put it, they had put the sun in the earth's place in the centre of the glorious temple of nature. The world had therefore a central body, as before, round which everything was arranged. The sun became the origin of a set of axes to which all motion in the cosmos could be related. But when Giordano Bruno deprived the sun of its central position, so that the world no longer had a centre which was at rest, a storm of fury was roused which could not be stilled. The Church could not make peace with this theory. For if Bruno was right, there was no longer anything stable to which man could orientate himself. Everything was reduced to fluctuation, and plunged, so to speak, into a whirlpool. The whole history of the relations between faith and astronomy offers clear proof of the fact that there is some kind of relation between the question, apparently one of pure physics, as to whether there is a body which is absolutely at rest, and the absoluteness of God in whom alone all absolutes are ultimately anchored.

8. THE DISRUPTION OF THIS FAITH IN A FIXED WORLD-CENTRE

The disruption of this faith in a fixed world-centre, or in a system of co-ordinates embracing the whole of world-reality, means a revolution whose effect from start to finish is either that faith in God is destroyed, or that it can emerge completely renewed and deepened. We must trace this process through its chief stages. It was not initiated by scientific discoveries or experiments. These came into the story only at a late stage, to deliver the knock-out blow. At the beginning there was natural philosophy, reflective considerations which rested on pre-scientific discoveries. Thus, for instance, navigation on the Mediterranean provided the point of departure from a theory of the flat earth.

The course of reflection, in whose final stages we are now involved, had already been set in train when, according to the Copernican Revolution, the earth ceased to be the world-centre which is at rest, and which contained the origin of a co-ordinate system whose axes spanned the entire universe. Once the ground of this absolute system of reference, which afforded man a secure purchase, had been removed by Copernicus, Kepler and Galileo, men were plunged into an unstable environment. Their condition was like that of the crew of a wrecked ship, who have taken to the waves, and are clinging either to a life-boat, or to a plank if the life-boat is already swamped, in an effort to keep above water. First the sun seemed for a time to offer support, when it temporarily took over the rôle of a central star at rest, which rôle the earth had been playing hitherto. But this was only a transitional phase. Already, following Galileo, mathematical physics had begun to reckon with the possibility that there could be no co-ordinate system in universal space which is fixed once for all, to which all motions can be referred. It was said that all co-ordinate systems are mutually equivalent, and any one can be displaced by another by a process of 'translation', without violence or distortion. This is the so-called classical relativity principle: Rest is equivalent to uniform motion. The truth of this law is impressed upon us time after time in everyday experience. Suppose we are on the deck of an ocean liner, which is travelling in a straight line with constant speed through a calm sea. We drop a heavy object, and it falls vertically. We play table-tennis, and the balls behave exactly as they would on a table on land. Their behaviour is affected only when the ship slows down or swings round in the vicinity of a harbour. In this classical relativity principle, the possibility which upsets all previous expositions comes into view for the first time, namely that there may be no absolute co-ordinate system, but rather an infinite number of systems of reference each equivalent to the others. From this, the far-reaching conclusion was quickly drawn that every law of nature, for instance Newton's gravitation law, must be so expressed, if it is to be universally applicable, that it can be transposed into any other co-ordinate system you like to choose among those which can displace one another by 'translation' without violence or distortion, and yet its form will remain unaltered. The fundamental equations used to express the law must therefore, to put it mathematically, be invariant with respect to all 'translatory' moving systems. This is the so-called Galileo-transformation. The avalanche was set in motion by this classical relativity-principle (C.R.P.), which put an infinity of possible frames of reference in place of a single absolute one. But a barrier cropped up which brought the rolling avalanche to a halt. The barrier lay in the fact that there are not merely mechanical movements of bodies carried out in empty space. Besides these, there are quite different events which cannot be reduced to the mechanical motion of bodies; in particular there is light, which Maxwell had recognized to be a special case of electro-magnetic radiation. This brought up the question: How can light waves travel through empty space? They travel unhampered through space which contains no air from the sun to the planets. There must be some medium, of which they are in fact the vibrations, just as air is the medium by which sound waves are propagated. And this led to the hypothesis that universal space is filled with something, the ether, through which the sun and the planets move without meeting any resistance, but which is sufficiently incompressible to afford a material medium for transverse light waves. If this is the case, then an ample substitute has been found for the central body which is at rest, which had become a lost cause from the time of the Copernican Revolution. In place of a single stellar body from which to establish the absolute co-ordinate system, there was a corporeal entity at rest which filled the entire cosmic space. Bodies in this space were then able to carry out motions which could be related, in accordance with the C.R.P., to any chosen system of co-ordinates. Yet such bodies were comparable with ships passing each other in the cosmic ocean, and having definite relative motions among themselves, each of them being at any moment located at a particular point on the ocean surface which could be plotted on a chart in respect of longitude and latitude. Their motions in relation to one another are relatively determinable, but they are absolutely determinable in relation to the ocean itself which is at rest.

Already, before the physical experiments were made which in the judgment of most physicists dealt the death blow to the old hypothesis of a material ether, men were aware that the hypothesis of a material ether as the carrier of light waves gave rise to insoluble problems. If the ether is to be regarded as a stuff at all, then it must be either solid or liquid or gaseous. If we think of it as solid, then it is beyond understanding that cosmic bodies should be able to move through it without meeting any resistance. If their motion is through a liquid ether-sea, then the work done in such a motion must be substantially affected, as in the case of a strong swimmer who wastes a certain amount of energy because of friction and whose rate of progress is thus slower than it might be. The hypothesis of ether being a gaseous stuff, and thus a kind of atmosphere, was abandoned by Fresnel because of the contemporary thesis that light was propagated in the form of transverse waves which seemed possible only in a solid medium, not a liquid or a gaseous one.

Before the ether-hypothesis was fully developed, Newton felt instinctively certain that since the Copernican Revolution it was highly problematic in any circumstances to try and anchor the fixed world co-ordinate system which he needed for his mechanical world-laws to cosmic bodies of any kind, great or small, sun, earth, or ether. He therefore took a bold and unprecedented step which carried man's search for an absolute point of rest to new lengths. He rejected any material foundation upon which to erect the scaffolding we need for taking measurements. He took one bold leap from the firm shore of corporeality and entrusted himself to empty space and empty time, to the forms of existence which remain when we abstract all the bodies which fill space and move in time. Newton, who believed in the exclusive validity of Euclidean geometry, took space and time to have a fixed structure, which provides an unshakable foothold for all the natural laws we formulate. The human measurements of space and time, to which all our sense-perceptions are reducible, cannot help but be inexact and relative; but behind our relative measurements, which are all that is possible to the senses, stands an absolute measurement, an ultimate reference point of absolute space and absolute time, structures which we grasp in mathematical thinking. Newton laid down:

'I. Absolute, true and mathematical time, of itself, and from its own nature, flows equably without relation to anything external, and by another name is called duration: relative, apparent, and common time, is some sensible and external (whether accurate or unequable) measure of duration by the means of motion, which is commonly used instead of true time; such as an hour, a day, a month, a year.

'II. Absolute space, in its own nature, without relation to anything external, remains always similar and immovable. Relative space is some movable dimension or measure of the absolute spaces; which our senses determine by its position to bodies; and which is commonly taken for immovable space; such is the dimension of a subterraneous, an aerial, or celestial space, determined by its position in respect of the earth. . . .

And so, instead of absolute places and motions, we use relative ones; and that without any inconvenience in common affairs; but, in philosophical disquisitions, we ought to abstract from our senses, and consider things themselves, distinct from what are only sensible measures of them. For it may be that there is no body really at rest, to which the places and motions of others may be referred.'[1]

Newton believed it possible to give an experimental proof that there is this absolute space. He based this proof on the fact that the movements of bodies in space are determined not merely by impact and reaction and mutual attraction, but, over and above all this, by the law of inertia, which he distinguished clearly from the law of gravitation. Impact, reaction and gravitational effect, as exercised by a body, can only be established when a second body is present in relation to which the first one moves. With the force of inertia, matters are quite different. To establish this, it is sufficient to have only one body, which is in empty space. Take, for example, a vessel filled with water, and rotate it. There is firm ground for deciding whether there is a real rotation in absolute space, or whether there is only an appearance of circular motion. If the vessel really revolves, then centrifugal forces will operate by the law of inertia, and the water will gradually rise at the sides of the vessel. If, however, there is only an appearance of circular motion in the vessel, or in other words if the vessel appears to rotate because I myself am moving round it in the reverse direction on a kind of roundabout, then the surface of the water will remain at rest. In this way, Newton said, one can find the direction as well as the magnitude of this circular motion in the infinitely great and empty space relative to which the motion takes place, even though there is nothing outward or knowable to be found as regards this space.

This experimental proof was the chief prop for Newton's faith in the absoluteness of Euclidean space and of its structure. It was impossible, on the level of natural science, to contradict the experimental proof, but the intrinsic impossi-

---

[1] Newton: *Philosophiae naturalis principia mathematica, Scholium ad Definitiones.* Cajori's edition, pp. 6 and 8.

bility of it was brought to light by means of certain fundamental convictions reached in mathematical logic. Leibnitz
attacked Newton's theory of absolute space, calling it a 'typical
English idea', an *idole de quelques Anglais modernes*. He
regarded this absolute geometrical space, and also absolute
time devoid of things, as an 'imagination', a pure abstraction.
For, in the view of Leibnitz, an extension without an extended
thing is an attribute without a subject. It was however Neumann, in his famous discourse 'On the Principles of the
Galileo-Newtonian theory' (1870), who first demonstrated
clearly the mathematical impossibility of an absolute motion.
The philosopher Vaihinger adopted Neumann's fundamental
ideas in his *Philosophie des Als-Ob* (*Philosophy of the 'As-If'*),
the basic parts of which were written by 1876-77. Neumann
showed that Galileo and Newton had formulated their laws
so that they could propound an absolute motion—Galileo
implicitly, and Newton quite avowedly. According to Galileo,
the law of inertia could be stated thus: a material point which
is set in motion continues to move in a straight line, and covers
equal distances in equal intervals of time, provided it is left
completely alone and that it is not affected from any other
source. The sentence thus framed, said Neumann, is utterly
incomprehensible. We do not know what is to be understood by motion in a straight line. For instance, a motion
which appears to be in a straight line from a point of view on
the earth, will be curved from a point of view on the sun, and
if it is viewed from Jupiter or Saturn or any other heavenly
body, it will appear in each case to be represented by a different kind of curve. The circular motion which the moon
has, seen from the earth, obviously changes its form when seen
from the sun, and is no longer represented by a circle but by
a spiral. Therefore, if the sentence is to mean anything, there
must be some special body in the universe to serve as a basis
for all our judgment, in relation to which all movements
ought to be assessed. The theoretical construction provided
by Galileo and Newton postulates that all motions in the
universe, actual and conceivable, must be related to one and
the same body. What is the body to which we must accord
this central place? Galileo and Newton gave no answer to

this question. If we want to give any kind of answer to it, we have to say that the ultimate principle of the Galileo-Newtonian thesis must be expressed as follows: that at some unknown point of universal space, there is an unknown body, and, further, an absolutely rigid body, one whose shape and dimensions remain for all time unalterable. Let us call it the alpha-body. This body must be a system of rigidly connected points, three being the minimum number of such points; or of rigidly connected straight lines, of which there are at least two. By the motion of a point, we are to understand its change of place, not in relation to the earth or to the sun, but only in relation to this alpha-body. Not only the law of inertia, but also the law of gravitation, and the concept of mass which both involve, are only definable in a Galileo-Newtonian sense, on the supposition of this alpha-body.

But how does this supposition come to be made? There is no empirical way of getting to it. From the scientific point of view it is arbitrary and unintelligible. Vaihinger, in *Die Philosophie des Als-Ob,* says that we are obliged by experience 'to see every motion as a relative one, which means that the system of co-ordinates which is being used is itself related to another system which is conceived as fixed, and that it is taken to have a motion of its own with respect to this fixed system, and so on *ad infinitum.* For what we really get, in any isolated instance of a perception of motion, is the increasing or diminishing approximation of two bodies to one another. And it is impossible to decide which of the two bodies is moving, or whether both of them are, without extra assistance given by a third point which is taken to be at rest. But because the state of rest attributed to the third point can only be established with reference to a fourth point which is also taken to be at rest, it is clear that we are being led into an infinite regress. It follows, therefore, that it is an impossibility to decide, in the empirical world, whether a given body is at rest or in motion. But, on the other hand, the mathematical physicist cannot express any motion in a formula, indeed a motion cannot be represented at all, unless it be implicitly related to an absolute point of reference which does not move, i.e. apart from the hypothesis that absolute space is an im-

movable co-ordinate system with three axes.' We are bound
to think of these world-axes intersecting at a certain fixed
point. And about this Vaihinger goes on to say: 'We have
no such thing. There being no such thing, one has to be
created by a hypothesis, and there lies the skill, the remarkable ingenuity, of the mechanist. An empirical point which
satisfies the requirements stated above cannot possibly be
found. Therefore an ideal point is assumed, which serves
the same purpose. It is in these terms that Neumann also
understands his alpha-body.' The firmly rooted point-system
which we need in order to make any spatial or temporal
measurement is thus a postulate of the thinking human mind,
a necessary fiction in which men are obliged to indulge if they
are to specify any motion or formulate any natural law. In
1870-80, therefore, the development started by the Copernican
revolution came to a provisional end with this postulate, of
a mid-point at rest within empty Euclidean space.

If then we look back over the stages through which the
development passed, we can say this. The successive stages
on the road did not come in any random order. Each step
in the development arose by necessity out of the previous one,
like sections of the track followed by a stone when it rolls
down a steep slope and comes to rest only at the lowest point.
The Copernican discovery acted like an earthquake upon the
firm ground where man had settled and put up his measuring
instruments, and he had to leave his old home and search in
a wider context for the fixed point which he needed. He
sought it first in the solar system, and later in the purely
hypothetical all-pervasive ether. When all such physical
anchorages slipped from under him, he made a bold mental
leap into empty space, by affirming its mathematical structure
to be absolute. But he soon discovered that by this attempt
to anchor himself in empty space, he had tumbled into a
bottomless pit. For space, as Leibnitz had already seen, is a
pure abstraction when it is emptied of things; a mere attribute
without a subject. The Archimedean point to which we are
able to relate ourselves is nowhere to be found in empty space.
It can only be postulated.

9. THE SPECIAL RELATIVITY THEORY: A FRUIT OF THE
DISRUPTION OF FAITH IN A FIXED WORLD-CENTRE

How does the development proceed, once this point has
been reached? As yet we cannot see the goal towards which
it is progressing, but we can see the direction in which it must
go forward from an inner necessity. The direction became
clear from the conclusion which Neumann reached. He maintained that man has embarked on a bold voyage of discovery, to
find, somewhere in the objective world outside himself, a
substitute for that which the fixed earth had been to him in
the days of the Ptolemaic world-picture; something absolute,
given purely objectively, outside ourselves and independent of
ourselves. The discovery reached at the end of the voyage
was that no such absolute point of rest to which our measurements can be anchored is in fact available in the objective
world, so long as we keep our own selves out of the matters
under consideration. We can only find the absolute when we
stop abstracting from ourselves and put ourselves back into the
picture. What happens then is that we determine for ourselves the absolute point of rest which we need; we invent it,
or postulate it. Neumann rightly saw that this postulated
point-system is the nail which must first be driven in so that
everything else which is necessary for the exact description of
nature may hang upon it. He saw that all spatial quantities
stand or fall with this fundamental postulate, and that the
same is true of all decisions as to whether lines are straight or
curved. He even recognized that all measurements of time
depend on it as well, though he expressed this differently from
the way in which we should express it today. What he said
was that if we are to decide whether two stretches of time are
equal, we can have no other means of reference than equal
movements of some material system, as for instance the rota-
tions of the earth. Therefore, he said, 'we can define equal
time intervals as those in which a point subject to no interference covers equal distances'. But the equality of distances
can only be determined from the alpha point-system. Ultimately, therefore, time depends on the system of spatial relations which we happen to choose.

Any further development from this point can only take place along the lines of providing physical confirmation of this postulate which so far rests on the ground of mathematical conviction, the postulate being that all spatio-temporal measurement depends on the choice of a system of reference. This, in turn, must mean that the task laid upon natural science by the formulation of the classical relativity principle must be taken up again on a higher level. What was required then was to state laws of nature in fundamental equations whose form does not depend on the choice of any particular system of reference, and which are therefore invariant with respect to such systems. But now a new goal is in sight, of which science had previously been unaware, namely to lay hold of an objective state of affairs which lies beyond all intuitive pictures of reality and can only be expressed in mathematical formulae. For the fundamental equations which are invariant with respect to the choice of reference system are objective regularities which can only be expressed mathematically, and can no longer be described as intuitive representations. In the time of the Galileo-transformation, however, calculations were still in terms of absolute time measurement, and of systems interchangeable by linear substitution, so that translation from one to another could be done without violence or distortion. Granted Neumann's thesis, this limitation disappeared and now we have to reckon with time as a variable magnitude depending on the system of reference, and with systems of reference whose relations to each other involve both curvature and acceleration. Cosmic reality as it is grasped in this fashion cannot be grasped intuitively at all. Its form is purely mathematical.

The next step in the development was that the ether, the last available material anchorage for an absolute co-ordinate system, was called into question, and not only by logico-mathematical reasoning as had hitherto been the case. The American scientists, Michelson and Morley, showed by experiment in 1887 that there were grave objections to a theory of the ether as the medium in which light is propagated, objections which could be met only with the aid of dubious artificial constructions. If there is a cosmic ocean of ether at rest, then the earth, on its annual circuit of the sun, moves through it like a zeppelin with a speed of thirty kilometres per second. Now if a light-signal is sent out from a particular point on the earth, in a direction against the motion of the earth, the light wave which is propagated in the ether-ocean ought to reach another point on its course and be caught there in a mirror after a shorter time than would be the case if the earth were at rest in the ether. For the goal of its journey is moving towards it all the time. The circumstances are precisely the same as when a child, standing on a railway platform beside which a train is moving, throws a ball parallel with the train but in the opposite direction to its motion. The ball takes less time to get to the end of the train than it would if the train were at rest. For the back of the train is coming to meet the ball all the time. On the other hand, if the light-signal is sent out in the same direction as that of the earth's motion, it ought to take longer to reach a point on the earth's surface than one would expect for that distance. Its goal is moving away all the time. It is as though the child threw his ball after a moving train. In these cases, the law of the addition and subtraction of velocities holds good, and the difference between the relative velocities of the light to the earth in both cases affords a basis for determining the exact velocity of light in the ether. Michelson and Morley did their best to establish the difference in time by precise measurement. They repeated the experiment several times, using every variety of technical device. But they could find no difference at all. In whatever direction light was sent out from this rapidly moving earth, east, west, north or south, it took the same time to reach destinations at the same distance from its origin. It was evidently the case that the earth, whatever direction it is moving in, carries the entire ether with it. Now at an earlier stage, in 1851, Fizeau had investigated the speed of light in a moving stream, using water moving at a known speed through a container. He reached the conclusion that the speed of light moving with such a stream is affected by the motion of the stream, though to a very slight degree. In a stream of moving air, for instance, the effect is practically negligible. In the opinion of most scientists this seemed to rule out the hypothesis that the earth carries the ether with it in the way we are obliged to postulate if the Michelson-Morley experiment is to be reconciled with the ether-hypothesis. The negative result of such observations opened the way for a new definitive interpretation of the ether as an auxiliary aid in the description of nature. It could be accepted as a mental framework which appears to be indispensable to the representation of natural events, just as we think of an equatorial line running round the earth, which serves as a base from which to construct in our minds a network of lines covering the globe by reference to which any point on the earth's surface can be mapped. Similarly, according to Jeans, the ether is a 'necessary mental fiction'. The existence of the ether, however, cannot be demonstrated. If anyone wishes to maintain that the ether is real, the chief difficulty is to explain how it is possible that a substance so comprehensive and omnipresent as the ether must be taken to be can conceal its existence so completely and evade all possibility of discovery, and in fact can maintain its incognito so effectively that no trace of its existence can be found. If the cosmic bodies are in fact moving at tremendous speed through a sea of ether, if they are like fish-baskets trailed through the sea at great speed, having plenty of holes for the water to flow through, it is still the case that there should be some evidence of the streaming of the water within the baskets. For 'if the earth is rushing through the ether at a speed of sixteen hundred kilometres per second, then we have to believe that the ether is flowing through this room at a rate of sixteen hundred kilometres per second, like a wind through trees. In fact, all the natural phenomena inside this room remain completely unaffected by this tremendous wind . . . and they would still be exactly the same if the wind were blowing at sixteen thousand kilometres per second—or if there were no wind at all ' (Jeans: *The Mysterious Universe*). There is no trace whatever of this 'ether-wind'. In view of all these considerations, it is no longer possible to use a material ether-substance as a foundation which is at rest, upon which may be constructed an absolute co-ordinate system.

When this conclusion was reached, and the last material

foundation had been destroyed upon which could rest the house of a Ptolemaic universal co-ordinate system, it seemed at first sight as though the foundations of any objective description of nature had also collapsed, and that there was nothing objective any more. On the contrary, there appeared now to be nothing but a topsy-turvy collection of cine-camera photographs, all taken from points with different perspectives, and all lines and masses were different on each of them. But it often happens that when the groundwork of a building is removed, older and deeper foundations are exposed whose existence had never been suspected because they lay so deep in the earth. The dismantling of the foundations of the former 'objective world-picture' laid bare a more profound and more firmly rooted objectivity. The dismantling of Ptolemaic objectivity, resting on a single world co-ordinate system, revealed at a deeper level an objectivity which affords complete independence of all changes in the system of reference. The first constituent of this deeper objectivity, disclosed by the demolition of the last relics of the Ptolemaic picture, was the constancy of the speed of light. The experiments which had called into question the hypothesis of an ether-substance at rest had revealed that light radiates in all directions from its origin with the same velocity, 299,792·5... kilometres per second by earthly measurement, independently of whether the cosmic body from which it originates is moving or at rest. The speed of light, c, Eddington called the 'limiting velocity'. For 'as the velocity of a material particle approaches the speed of light, its mass increases to infinity. From this it follows that it is impossible for it to have a velocity greater than that of light. This conclusion follows from the laws of special relativity, and investigation has so far gone to confirm it with very high velocities.' Therefore the speed of light plays the part of a limiting velocity, just as, classically, an infinite velocity did. Whatever moves with the speed of light is in effect moving infinitely fast, for it is able to cover any distance at all without occupying a fraction of a second in which to do so. If a man were to do so, he would be like Ahasuerus coming back to find the world five hundred years older than when he left, while he himself has not advanced at all towards his death. He would have experienced nothing at all on his journey. The five hundred earthly years would for his consciousness have been slept away. If he remained conscious on the journey, he would have experienced eternity in a moment, were it not for the fact that he would require eternity in which to think a single thought. Time does not exist for him. Our space, also, would not exist for him, for the distance between two stars which he happened to pass would shrink to nothing.

In a previous section, we saw that rigid matter has now resolved itself in modern physics into an event, and that this event is light, taking the widest sense for that term. For light and electricity tend to coincide. Now it has been shown that the speed with which the event happens is a constant limiting velocity which is a foundation measurement for all velocities found in the world.

Given this conclusion, the next decisive step towards a new understanding of 'objective reality' was the discovery that not only was an absolute ether-substance which is at rest an untenable hypothesis, but that the mathematical hypothesis, which had enabled Newton to dispense with a material point of rest and yet have an absolute standard of measurement, was also untenable, viz. the assumption that there is 'absolute, true and mathematical time' and 'absolute space'. Once the speed of light had been established as a limiting velocity, a method was propounded by which to determine the simultaneity of two world events; to decide, in other words, whether two clocks at points x_1 and x_2, say at York and Newcastle, were in fact keeping the same time. It was shown, quite simply, that the determination of simultaneity according to this method varies according to the state of motion of the body from which it is carried out. Imagine an incredibly long railway train stretching from York to Newcastle. The front of the train is at the point x_1, and the end at x_2. The train leaves York exactly at noon, and simultaneously the last coach leaves Newcastle. In the middle of the train there is a V-shaped pair of mirrors which reflect rays of light to an observer in a direction perpendicular to the movement of the train. If light-signals are sent out from York and Newcastle, and this observer sees the two light-flashes at the same time, it follows that the two light signals were sent out at the same time, and therefore that the clock in York keeps the same time as the clock in Newcastle, or that they are 'synchronized'. A passenger sitting in the train will therefore say that a light-signal sent from the engine, and one sent from the last coach, are emitted simultaneously if the two rays coming from each of those points meet in the middle of the train. And in fact two such signals, sent out 'simultaneously' do meet at the mid-point of the track between York and Newcastle. But when the train is in motion, the mid-point of the train is no longer the mid-point of the track. These mid-points would be identical if the train were at rest. But it has begun to move. While the two signals have each been covering their half of the journey, the train has travelled forward, and the meeting point of the two light rays, seen with reference to the train, is further back towards Newcastle than the actual mid-point of the train. The passenger, sitting in the train, and thinking and measuring from the standpoint of the train, is then obliged to say that the Newcastle clock is slow. Naturally such a difference is barely noticeable, and is completely insignificant from the point of view of technical communications, since the speed of light is so incredibly great. If the speed of light were significantly less, or if a train could travel at a speed approaching that of light, the discrepancy would be so striking that the whole business of railway travel would be entirely disordered. What we have here are two conflicting points of view. The first is that of the station-masters at York and Newcastle, whose reference-system is the earth's solid ground. From this point of view, the two clocks are in time with each other. This can readily be confirmed by someone standing at the mid-point of the stationary train, or at the mid-point of the track between the stations, and using the V-shaped mirror. The other point of view is that of the passenger who makes the experiment with the light-signals in the moving train, and deduces that the York clock is fast, or the Newcastle clock is slow. And there is justification for either point of view. There is in the universe no absolute alpha point-system by means of which we may decide what is at rest and what is in motion. The passenger is just as entitled to suppose that the train is at rest and that the ground is moving backwards underneath it, as are the station-masters entitled to regard the ground as stationary. We are therefore forced to conclude that 'there is no absolute simultaneity, and therefore no absolute time; time is relative to such a degree that every system has its own time'.[1]

Now our concern, in this context, is not with the physical implications, but rather with the implications for our world view, which follow from this state of affairs, which serves to open the road to the special relativity theory. Before going on, we ought to pause for a moment, and ask what possible philosophical significance there can be in such a state of affairs. Above all, we must try to be clear about the connection between this physical determination of simultaneity and time measurement, and what is directly known to us about the stream of time within which our whole existence is involved. If this business with mirrors and light-signals is looked at purely objectively from the standpoint of the scientific experimenter, the experiment has nothing to do with time itself, whose nature it is the task of philosophical thinking to elucidate. What can be established physically is always a physical event. Physically, however, the flow of time itself is not open to be perceived. All that can be perceived is the occurrence of some physical event, such as the circling of the planets round the sun, the motion of a pointer on a clock, the descent of a clock weight, or the flow of sand from the upper to the lower part of an hour-glass. Physically, as Neumann says, 'we can only define equal time intervals as those in which a point, subject to no outside interference, covers equal intervals of distance'.[2] It is only possible for us to use these physical events and investigate with their aid the simultaneity of two events, because we participate as conscious beings in the events, and take them into our consciousness. It is from this source that what we call simultaneity, or the relation of before and after, first emerges out of the correspondence and mutual

[1] A. Pflüger, *Das Relativitätsprinzip*, 1920, p. 124.
[2] H. Hermann makes a somewhat different proposal in his article *Gleichförmigkeit der Zeit und Uhrprüfung* in the periodical *Z. für Physik 20*, 1923.

ordering of physical events like the movement of a pointer or the motion of a star. In his profound meditation on the mystery of time in the *Confessions*, Augustine said: *in te, anima mea, tempora metior* (in thee, my soul, I measure times). Only when we are involved in the world-process as conscious beings do physical mysteries come to be experienced as the passage of time.

We can demonstrate this by reference to the imaginary experiment with the train. Suppose that the long train which stretches from York to Newcastle is entirely empty. There is no self-conscious being in it at all, not even an engine driver, but only machines and recording apparatus so arranged that the impact of the light rays on the mirrors is automatically noted. All that can then be said is this. When the train is standing still, the two light-rays meet at one place, and when it is in motion, they meet at another. The notion that inferences about certain time relationships can be made on the basis of these physical occurrences does not arise unless something other than mere recording apparatus plays a part, unless one conscious being at any rate participates in the total event and takes it into his consciousness. But one conscious mind is not enough if an inference is to be drawn from the experiment that there are two systems of reference, in one of which two events are simultaneous whereas in the other they are not. Let us suppose that only one mind is involved, and let us call it the person A. Let us suppose that this person is the station-master standing on the platform at York. In the train itself there is no human being, but simply physical apparatus. After the experiment, this person gathers from the recording apparatus that the two light-rays in fact met at a different point, when the train moved, from that at which they met when it stayed at rest. But he would never entertain the idea that the moving train was a reference-system with its own local time. He would assess the results from his own point of view, which is that of the ground at rest on which he stands, and he would say that quite naturally the light-rays must meet at a different point. The train was travelling away from New-castle and therefore away from the Newcastle light-signal. It was travelling towards the York light-signal. Therefore the meeting-point, which is half-way along the *track*, must lie further back along the *train* than its mid-point. Now if again we suppose that there is only one conscious being involved, but this time, instead of putting him on the platform, we let him be a passenger in the train, what happens? Let us call him person B, and let us suppose that he studies the whole event from a standpoint on the train, just as the station-master studies it from a standpoint on the ground which is at rest. In point of fact, this could hardly happen with any person in a train because we are so accustomed to regard a train in which we are sitting from the standpoint of the ground which is at rest, and we regard it as a moving train, not as a body which is at rest. But there are circumstances which make us uncertain about this for a moment or so, as for instance when another train moves in relation to ours on the next line, and we are not sure whether our train is standing still and the other is moving, or whether it is the other way round, or whether both trains are moving, but with different speeds or in different directions. One thing that becomes peculiarly clear in this event is that though we are able to oscillate between different points of view, we cannot adopt two different standpoints at the same time. Consciously or unconsciously, we have to decide at any moment in favour of a particular point of view. Once the decision is made, however, the choice of standpoint carries with it a self-contained system of reference in accordance with which all observed bodily motions, such as the flight of a bird or the fall of a stone, have a definite direction and speed. If, instead of travelling on the earth in a train, we were on a heavenly body, say the moon circling round the earth, then we should naturally and quite involuntarily take up the standpoint of the moon, and we should suppose the earth to be moving round us in the opposite direction to that which the moon now has. It would therefore be highly unusual, but nevertheless quite conceivable, that a passenger in a train should adopt the point of view that the train is at rest, and that the ground is moving backwards beneath it. If, with this standpoint, he discovered that light-signals sent out from the front and back of the train reached an apparatus fixed at the mid-point of the train at the same time, he would conclude that the light-signals were emitted simultaneously. Now suppose there is an apparatus at the mid-point of the track between York and Newcastle, and that it records automatically what happens, so that you can go to it after the event and read the result, as you can with a maximum and minimum temperature thermometer. When the passenger gathers that this apparatus has registered the fact that the light-rays met at a different point from that which was suggested by apparatus on the train, he will never entertain the idea that the railway track on which it is fixed is a different reference-system with its own local time and its own form of time-measurement. He will simply say that while the light-rays were on their journey, the earth was in motion and the track moved back under the train, and therefore moved towards the ray coming from Newcastle and away from that coming from York. And therefore the meeting-point of the two rays must lie nearer to Newcastle than to York. In both cases, therefore, we are left with a single system of reference to which the whole state of affairs is related.

An interpretation on quite different lines will be offered only in circumstances which involve not merely two unconscious recording machines and the presence of one person making his observations either from a platform or from a seat in the train, but where two conscious beings experience the event from two different standpoints. The case then becomes entirely different. When only one conscious being is involved, whether it is only A or only B, there can be no conflict. Either of these beings can explain the report given by a recording apparatus which is moving against the chosen frame of reference in physical terms, without undue effort, and incorporate it into his own system. But if two conscious beings are there at the same time, and each has to incorporate the other's report into his own reference system, there is bound to be tension. A is bound to say to B: 'By means of the mirrors I have established objectively that the two light-signals were sent out simultaneously. The clocks in York and Newcastle are therefore in time with one another.' B is bound to say to A: 'That is not correct. By means of my apparatus I have established objectively that the light-signals were sent off one after the other. The Newcastle clock is slow. 1 am, in fact, a little older than it suggests.' If there were a co-ordinate system which is absolutely at rest, it would enable a decision to be made as to which of these persons was right, and the conflict between them could be smoothed out in terms of classical physics. But there is no impartial court of appeal which can give a verdict as between A and B, for there is no alpha-point which is fixed absolutely, independent of our own preference. Both standpoints, therefore, have equal justification. They oppose one another as two reference-systems which are equally justified. The motion of a body seen with reference to one of the systems will follow a different line from that which it takes when seen with reference to the other. Not only do the motions of bodies yield different lines and different curves, but there is also a difference in time-measurements, and a different decision about questions concerning the simultaneity of two events, according as one or the other system is used.[1] It was recognized, of course, in classical physics, that if the motion of a body is photographed from two different standpoints, then quite different pictures may result. But it was only with the advent of relativity theory that the measurement of time came to be regarded as a matter of relativity, and was dealt with from that point of view in mathematical calculation.

From all this we see that the fact that there are many equally justified co-ordinate systems, within which different local times obtain, cannot be ascertained merely by setting up recording apparatus such as clocks and mirrors at various points of space. The state of affairs which can be read off from such apparatus is in itself susceptible of a different interpretation. To reach the idea that there are many systems of reference with equal claims to justification, we are necessarily thrown back on to the fact that conscious beings participate in world events; or, more precisely, that we ourselves

[1] The text-books on relativity theory will explain why these considerations are not invalidated by suggestions made for comparing times by moving clocks about. There is, indeed, an instance of something like this transport of clocks, which confirms the dilation of time. The mesons in cosmic radiation would never reach the earth if their disintegration were not noticeably retarded through their high velocity.

stand within the experienced world at a particular point where we have been set irrevocably by a mysterious and fateful decision, and share in what we experience. This placing, through which we exist, is of decisive importance for us in respect of all the questions which have to be raised in this book, for, as we saw earlier, the question about God comes up in intimate connection with it. It is therefore of very great significance that through this placing, which raises the question of God, we are given the mid-point of a reference-system within which all events of the objective world which are discernible from that point must be ordered. This centre for all perspectives may be at rest. It may also be in motion. In that case there will arise a new picture of all events. What happens will be photographed from a new standpoint. The peculiarity of this unique placing, which is of existential importance to all of us, is, however, that the centre for our perspective, to which everything is related, can only be at one place at any given time, and not simultaneously at many places. The realm of consciousness of a conscious being therefore posits one system of reference only, at any one moment, with one definite local time. If there are to be many equally justified systems there together, then there must be many conscious beings, or at any rate, an I and a Thou, who contemplate the world together from different standpoints. If we ignore all conscious beings, and study what happens in itself, so to speak, without any regard for them, then what happens has no definite time scale. Such a scale is there only when there is a given system of reference. And this is posited by a conscious being.

There is quite a simple way in which we can conceive this state of affairs. It has already been mentioned that different living things have different time-rates. Just as is the case among men, so there can be other beings some of which experience the same events more slowly. A may-fly, whose nuptial flight is also its death flight, has a quicker time-rate than a human being. In the few hours of a summer evening, a may-fly rises from the river bank to perform its wedding dance in the air with its thousand sisters, and falls back, dying, to be carried away by the dark stream. Between those moments this delicate creature clearly goes through, in a compressed form, all the wealth of experience which in man's case lasts out through the span of human life—it is born, it marries, it dies. A plant, on the other hand, so far as we can tell, seems to have a much slower time-rate than a man. What to us is a day, is for a plant only time enough to take one breath. If in any sense a plant enjoys consciousness, then in one day it experiences no more than does a human being between a couple of heart-beats. We can easily think of other beings whose time-rate is much faster even than that of a may-fly. It must therefore be conceivable that there is a being whose time-rate reaches the upper limit of possibility. This would mean that for such a being, the whole of universal history, which at our time-rate stretches over millions of years, is compressed into a moment. For such a being, there would be no time at all. Everything would be compressed into an eternal moment (*nunc aeternum*). If this is even conceivable, we are bound to draw the conclusion that the 'objective world', which is experienced at different rates by different beings, would therefore, in itself (if we were able to abstract from all conscious beings), have no time-rate. It simply presents a manifold, which, if it is experienced at all, must be experienced in a particular order. The speed with which it moves through this order can take any selected value. It may vary between zero and infinity. The time-rate, which can be anything from very slow to very fast, first comes into the picture when conscious beings are there to experience what happens from different standpoints. Thus there is no objective simultaneity, and no objective before-and-after relationship. 'The physical world, the object, of perception . . . has no temporality, nothing happens in it, it simply is.'[1]

The new and more deeply rooted objectivity, which has come to light since the demolition of the old Ptolemaic objectivity, can no longer be represented in perceptual terms. For what happens in the world is only open to perception when it takes place in a time which flows along at a constant

---

[1] A. Wenzl, *Wissenschaft und Weltanschauung* (*Science and World-view*) p. 124. Cf. also his *Philosophie der Welt und Naturwissenschaft* (*Philosophy of the World, and Natural Science*) p. 82.

rate. We are not able to represent to ourselves a world which can shrink to an instant of time. The objective reality, upon whose foundations we are now stumbling, must lie on the further side of the conflict between all systems of time and space measurement which may seem appropriate. But, if we wish to get behind the conflicting co-ordinate systems, the only thing we are able to formulate and establish objectively is the fact that we can work out the mathematics of all space-time measurements which occur within the various systems and exhibit their relationship. This fact clearly indicates that an all-inclusive unity lies behind the conflicting systems, and that they are all held within it. The fact that measurements in terms of one system can be dealt with in terms of another has a significance similar to the fact that the currencies of different countries can be used convertibly for trade. This is possible only because behind the various currencies there lies a single standard of value applicable to all of them, within which all kinds of money may be embraced, the standard being that of human need. The possibility of convertibility between the various systems of measurements has a similar significance. If I know the measurable relations within my own world-picture, and also know the direction and velocity with which another reference system moves in relation to my own, I can calculate the measurements with which the other being is bound to view the same realities. Relativity theory goes beyond Galileo only in this, that in the calculation it must be remembered that not only space measurement but also time measurement depends on the standpoint of the observer. This is the difference between the equations of the Lorentz transformation and those of the Galileo transformation where only space relationships enter into the calculation. The fact that it is possible to work out the relationship not only of space-systems, but the far more complicated matter of time-systems, shows that there is something real which extends over all systems, and remains constant in any change of system. This all-embracing unity has been most clearly expressed in Minkowski's four-dimensional world-continuum, where the fourth axis is taken to represent the time-measurement multiplied by $\sqrt{-c^2}$ (c being the velocity of light, 300,000 kilometres per second). This four-dimensional space-time continuum has a geometry which differs from ordinary four-dimensional Euclidean geometry only in the fact that the time co-ordinate is an imaginary number whilst the space co-ordinates are real numbers. An imaginary number is defined as one whose square is a negative number, whereas a real number by definition is one whose square is a positive number. The imaginary three ($i3$) multiplied by itself is -9. Apart from this difference in the sign of the product, calculations in terms of imaginary numbers are just like those which use real numbers. The special geometry of the four-dimensional continuum with its imaginary time-axis may be called pseudo-Euclidean with respect to the time-axis. The principle in virtue of which time and space make up a uniform pseudo-Euclidean continuum in the fundamental equations of physics is called the principle of relativity.

The principle states that it must be possible to rotate the reference-system of the four axes by means of which the points of the world are identified with three spatial co-ordinates and one temporal co-ordinate, and that however one does so the *form* of the fundamental equations of physics remains unaltered. By such a rotation, the time-axis will be taken to lie in a different direction. To make calculations in terms of the new position of the axes, we must use the trigonometrical functions (sine, cosine and tangent) of the angles which the new axes make with the old ones. In working out the mathematics of the pseudo-Euclidean geometry, it becomes evident that the angle through which the time-axis has been rotated must be reckoned as an imaginary quantity. The trigonometrical functions of an imaginary angle are worked out by reference to precisely the same formulae as obtain in the case of real quantities, and the only thing to watch is the difference of sign in multiplication. But this has the effect of producing a quite essential difference. Every trigonometrical function of a real angle is periodic. Every time the angle increases by 360° (a complete revolution), the function in question, sine, cosine or tangent, takes the same values in the same sequence as in the previous cycle. But the trigonometrical functions of an imaginary angle continue to increase. The 'rotation' of the imaginary time-axis is a different kind of behaviour from the rotation of a real co-ordinate axis in Euclidean space. When the imaginary time-axis 'rotates', it does not return periodically to its initial position. It moves further and further away from it, though more and more slowly as the 'rotation' proceeds, and it tends towards an imaginary infinite limiting magnitude which it never reaches.

Now the time-axis may be given a 'rotation' in any number of initial directions, and if we plot all the limits to which it can tend within the four-dimensional space-time system, they compose a three-dimensional continuum which surrounds the original time-axis in just the same way as the surface of a cone in ordinary three-dimensional space surrounds its central axis. Thus whatever rotation is given to the original reference-system (the four axes in the space-time continuum), the time-axis must always lie *within* this cone of limiting directions which we may call the limiting cone. However great the rotation may be, say to t^1, t^1 never can lie on or beyond the limiting cone. At the same time it may be shown that the space-axes which rotate with the time-axis (x moving to x^1) always remain *outside* the limiting cone. Pseudo-Euclidean geometry therefore implies that temporal and spatial directions always remain strictly separate, and it is impossible to carry through any rotation of the reference-system by means of which the time-axis is transformed continuously into a space-axis, or a space-axis into a time-axis. Further, because the time-axis t can only be moved, by however great a rotation, within the limited range afforded by the limiting cone, it can never be rotated so much as to be reversed, so that the directions of past and future are interchanged. Whatever rotation we choose to give to the set of four axes, the past remains always past and future always future. The limiting cone is of course a double cone, a past cone and a future cone. These meet in an apex, an origin, which is the present. Outside this limiting time-cone, any line of spatial direction, say the x-axis, can be completely rotated so that the original directions, forward and backward, are interchanged.

Therefore, although time and space together compose a uniform four-dimensional continuum, the generally recognized distinctions between spatial and temporal lines of direction are maintained by the pseudo-Euclidean geometry of the continuum.

If now in a reference-system S (and it will be sufficient to think simply of a time-axis and *one* space-axis, say the x-axis), a given point is at rest, then for every value of t its x-co-ordinate will be the same. Its 'world-line' is therefore parallel to the t-axis. If now we effect a transposition to another set of axes, t^1, x^1, by a rotation of the kind discussed, then the 'world-line' of the point will no longer be parallel to the time-axis which is now t^1. We can take this as evidence that the new system S^1 is one which is in motion with respect to S. The effect is that we can regard the S^1 system as one in which the angle between the t^1 and x^1 axes is no longer a right-angle but is acute.

It may be possible to shed further light on this very difficult conception by an illustration based on the familiar fact that, in a film, single moments in a temporal happening can be spread out in a spatial sequence of photographs. This provides a simple method of demonstrating how time may be regarded as a fourth axis added to a three-dimensional Euclidean space-system. Suppose that it is a moving car which is being filmed. If the film strip is cut up into separate photographs, and these are put in order, one on top of another, then the vertical direction in which the pack grows provides a spatial representation of the time dimension in which the event takes place. It is true that the photographs are flat or two-dimensional but their effect, like that of all pictures, is three-dimensional. The dimension of depth is projected on to the flat surface. These flat photographs represent moments in a three-dimensional event. Now take the pack of photographs, think of the four corners of the car on each one, and imagine lines drawn through the pack from bottom to top to touch the four corners on every picture. If the car was not moving, these will be straight lines perpendicular to the pack. If the car was moving, they will be inclined from the perpendicular, and the angle at which they slope will be greater according as the speed of the car is greater. These four lines which represent the moving car will then outline a sloping prism, and the slope of the prism increases with the speed of the car.   Lines which go through the pack from top to bottom represent, as we have said, the time-axis.   The fact that the lines have come to have this particular form depends on the camera-man having photographed the car from a fixed point on the ground; that is to say, on his choice of the earth as his reference system which is at rest.   This system, whose origin is on the earth, we will call S.   The film pack produced by a photographer who travels alongside the moving car in another car going at the same speed, will be different.   From the standpoint of this second camera-man, i.e. within a system S^1, the moving car will appear to be at rest.   The lines produced by the corners of the car will be perpendicular to the surface of his pack, and will therefore represent his time-axis.   We can see now how it is possible to combine the space and time measurements reached within two systems, S and S^1, for one and the same event.   Provided we know the speed at which the car which is being photographed travels, we do not need a second moving camera at all in order to construct the set of pictures which must be contained in any such S^1 pack.   We can do it by tilting the pack of S photographs, until the lines of what was a sloping prism are brought into the perpendicular.   But this means that the angle between the pack and the time-axis has been altered, in order to make the S pack conform to the S^1 pack.   Thinking now in terms of the S system, we conclude that the second photographer's results are produced because he is experiencing the event from within a co-ordinate system whose axes are oblique, and it is to these oblique axes that he has been relating all his measurements.   In the system S^1, the angle between the space-axes is less than a right-angle; but also the angle between the whole spatial system and the time-axis is less than a right-angle.   These two angles are in fact the same, and they may be taken to correspond to one another.   In a system which is at rest, both are right-angles. Now a unit of one second on the time-axis is equivalent to a unit of 300,000 kilometres on the horizontal space-axis.   If we try and picture this distortion of a system of axes from the rectangular to an oblique configuration, it is at once apparent that not measurements of distance only, but measurements of time will be affected.   In an oblique system, units both of length and of time will be increased by comparison with what they stood for in a rectangular system.   Therefore a rod whose length is measured with reference to S^1 will be shorter than when it is measured with reference to S, because the unit of measurement is increased.   Similarly, the time which an event takes according to a clock in S^1 will be shorter than the time indicated for the same event by a clock S, because in the oblique system the unit of time has been lengthened.[1]

Thus a new 'absolute' has taken the place of absolute mathematical space and absolute mathematical time, on which Newton based his physics so that he could reach conclusions of universal validity.   It is the four-dimensional world of Minkowski, the unobservable space-time continuum, within which space and time are simply axes of co-ordinates whose configuration depends on the state of motion of the observing subject, so that different kinds of system carry with them different space and time measurements.   The division of the continuum into space and time belongs therefore only to our subjective human way of looking at things.   'If we could take off our subjective human spectacles,' said Jeans, 'we should realize that an event does not happen at a point in space and a moment in time, but rather that it exists at a point of the continuum whose time and space comprise the event; and we should thus discover that the primary elements of nature are not *things,* existing in space and time, but *events* in the space-time continuum.   An event which is distinguished by its duration in time can now be regarded as a continuous series of events, in which each term in the series stands for the existence of the object in a moment of time and a point of space.'   If we call four-dimensional space-time the objective world-continuum, in contrast with subjective aspects of the

---

[1] The first part of this exposition of Minkowski's space-time continuum is taken from an article by Gustav Mie: *Die Göttliche Ordnung in der Natur* (*The Divine Order in Nature*), published in *Ethik*, 1937-38, p. 14.   The illustration from film-strips is Professor Heim's simplified version which alone appeared in the German edition of his book.   Following the advice of Dr. H. Hermann of Tübingen, the translator thought it proper to include the original account by Mie in this English edition, in order to expand the author's thought for the sake of the general reader.

world depending on the choice of a particular standpoint, we can in the same way make a distinction between subjective lines of space and stretches of time which arise within the different systems, and the objective 'world-lines'. A world-line is the line in the four-dimensional continuum which a particular object describes. We have a representation of it in the lines of the sloping prism produced by the motion of the car in the pack of photographs. Provided the car moves uniformly in a straight line in space, their world-lines are straight lines. If two cars move at the same speed, their world-lines will be parallel. If they move at different speeds, their world-lines tend towards one another. The 'interval' between two points on the objective world-lines, say the points which indicate the departure of a train from York and its arrival at Newcastle, is independent of whether the train's journey is described from the standpoint of the earth, i.e. as a motion during which it travels over the earth, or whether it is described from the point of view of the fireman, who stands on the same spot in front of the engine's firebox, and does a couple of hours hard work there.

10. THE GENERAL RELATIVITY THEORY: A FINAL CONSEQUENCE

Let us once again look back over the ground covered so far. It has appeared that the special relativity theory, which we have been talking about up to now, seen as a world-outlook, is the last stage in clearing up the ruins left by the demolition of Ptolemaic objectivity, which task was begun by Copernicus. It is the end of the last attempt man has made to find a world-centre which is at rest, and which is given to him, so to speak, from outside, independently of his own status. If this demolition, which has produced the relativizing of the world foundations as hitherto conceived, had indeed been the final goal of relativity theory, then it would be correct to say its destructive effects are all of a piece with the relativizing of the foundations of morality. But we saw that as soon as the foundation walls of the old world structure were laid in ruins, and the rubble cleared away, what has been done is a negative preparation for something positive, namely for the discovery of new and deeper-lying foundations, so that a new objectivity, which lies beyond the contradictions of all subjective world-pictures in a far deeper sense than did the Ptolemaic universe, is within our grasp. From this point of view, we must now glance briefly at the so-called general relativity theory, which provokes stronger opposition than the special. Seen as a world-outlook, it is simply an attempt to pursue the road followed by special relativity to its end, both in regard to its negative tendency whereby it demolishes the old objectivity, and in regard to its positive tendency towards the construction of a new objectivity. The special relativity principle has in view, as had Galileo, only the invariant quality of physics in respect of all systems moving uniformly and linearly in relation to one another, regarding them as equally warranted reference systems. All it has done is to extend the principles of Galileo into the fields of electro-magnetism and optics. The principle of general relativity acknowledges no such limits. Reference systems can move in relation to one another in ways other than those of linear and uniform motion. They may have a motion of rotation relative to one another, as is the case with the earth and the sun; and there may be a relative acceleration within their motions. When reference systems are in rotation, or are accelerated, in relation to one another, then naturally entirely different pictures of reality occur within these different systems. But even in these complicated relationships, it must be possible to combine the different measurements, provided the relative acceleration of the two systems is known, i.e. the curves which they follow in relation to one another. And it is requisite that this combining of measurements should not affect the form of the physical laws. Only when this is the case are all co-ordinate systems in universal space truly given the same warrant, whatever their relation to one another, even if that relation be one of relative acceleration, or if they rotate about each other. Once these ideas were thought through to their end, they involved the ruin of Newton's final experimental support for his theory of absolute mathematical space. He tried to show that it is possible to determine absolutely, even in empty space, what is moving and what is at rest. The experiment he proposed was the one with a vessel full of water, whose contents were forced up the sides of the vessel according to the law of centrifugal force provided the vessel is rotating, but maintain the same level when it is at rest. The experiment which most clearly exhibits the facts of the case where all reference systems have equal warrant, even those with relative acceleration or with rotatory motion, is one proposed by Einstein, where we think of an observer in a lift. Let us suppose there is a box, as big as a room, within universal space which otherwise is empty. An observer is within the box, and is unable to see anything outside it. If the universe is empty, then gravitation does not affect him. The attraction exerted by all the walls of the box is of equal effect. Therefore he has to attach himself to the floor with ropes, or the lightest blow he receives will set him moving in some direction. Now suppose that outside, above the ceiling of the lift, there is a hook to which a cable is attached. The observer inside can see neither hook nor cable. Suppose now that something pulls on the cable, and the lift moves upwards with uniform acceleration. The observer notices this simply by reason of a pressure on the soles of his feet. The floor presses against his feet. This pressure is explained by the law of inertia. According to the principle of inertia, the observer's body offers resistance to the upward motion. Now suppose that he drops a stone inside the box. It falls to the floor, for it does not share the upward acceleration of the lift. It remains stationary while the lift's floor is moving upwards. The stone behaves, in fact, exactly as though the floor of the lift were exerting an attractive force like that of gravitation. If the observer releases from his hand not merely a stone, but other objects such as an apple or a lead pellet, they will all fall at the same speed just as is the case with gravitation. In the case of gravitation as we experience it, it is of course the resistance of the air which makes a feather fall more slowly than a lead pellet. What conclusion may be drawn from this? One and the same event appears to be an effect of gravitation, when seen from the point of view of the observer in the lift, who supposes the lift to be at rest; but when seen from the standpoint of someone outside the lift, who knows about the cable, it appears to be an effect of inertial resistance. There is a gravitational field inside one system, whereas in the other there is no gravitational field. Thus Newton's experimental proof for distinguishing 'true' from 'apparent' motion breaks down. The centrifugal force on which it rests is only a case of the law of inertia. Suppose we have a circular disc in empty space, rotating uniformly about its centre. An observer sitting on the disc and near to its edge has to hold on firmly, or he will be thrown off. He feels the force which we understand to be an effect of inertia. But since space is empty, the observer has no point of reference by which to decide whether he is in motion or whether he is at rest. He may therefore suppose himself to be at rest, and the place where he is sitting will become the mid-point of a reference system. According to the centrifugal law, he is in danger of being thrown off along a particular tangent, but this tangent has shrunk to a mere direction from a point which to him is at rest. He must therefore explain the force, which is undoubtedly trying to throw him off the disc (which to him is not moving), as some kind of attraction from outside, which is being exerted upon the disc and upon himself. He takes it to be the effect of a gravitational field. But the mass-distribution corresponding to this field can in any case only be constructed for the particular point where he is, and not for the disc as a whole. If systems which rotate in relation to one another, or which are accelerated in relation to one another, are systems with an equal warrant, then both accounts of what is happening are equally justified. Therefore gravitation at once loses the exceptional status which previously it had enjoyed. According to the 'principle of equivalence', gravitation and inertia are in the last resort one and the same, being merely regarded from different points of view. Therefore the gravitational effect of the sun on the earth can be understood equally well as a movement of the entire medium within which are the sun and the earth, in a direction opposite to that of the gravitational effect. The whole event can be portrayed as the lifting upwards of an invisible box whose floor represents the sun, and where the earth is represented by a falling stone. Important consequences follow from this in connection with a light-ray emitted by a body like the sun or a star. Within a Galileo co-ordinate system, the ray is propagated in a straight line. But if we take the accelerated box as our reference body, the path of a light-ray, which appears from the first reference system to be straight, will seem to be curved. For think of a ray which comes into the box through a hole, and pursues its course through the box while the box is being moved upwards. This ray, relative to the box, will not follow a straight track but a curved one. The conclusion may therefore be drawn that, in gravitational fields, light-rays are in general propagated curvilinearly. For light-rays in our immediate neighbourhood the curvature is hardly noticeable, whereas it is quite apparent in the case of rays which pass close by the sun. This will be expressed in observations of fixed stars which seem to be in the neighbourhood of the sun during a total eclipse. By comparison with the place they have on our astronomical charts when the sun is in a different part of the sky, they will seem to have been displaced somewhat, because the rays from them have to pass so close to the sun.

In this context we will not embark on the question still under dispute, as to whether astronomical observation does indeed confirm the general relativity theory, or whether certain facts which have been taken as confirmation are susceptible of another explanation. (Cf. Thiessen in *Himmelswelt*, 1947, 55, p. 37.) Here we are only concerned with the basic philosophical thesis that the simultaneous justification of all systems, whatever their relative motion may be, from which general relativity theory tries to draw ultimate conclusions, is the direct line of advance along the road which natural science has been treading since the Copernican Revolution. Whether or not this road, carved out by human thought, is the right one, is not a matter which can be settled by pure observation and measurement. For we are obliged, in this 'box-experiment', as we were in the train-experiment, to make a clear distinction between the facts established by instruments, and the meaning of these facts, which only comes into the picture when conscious beings take part in it, and set the whole event within a space-time scheme.   In the bitter conflicts which have arisen about relativity theory, several misunderstandings on both sides might have been avoided if a clear enough distinction had been made in advance between the observed facts and their significance. In the case of the hypothetical experiment with the train, we saw that if only one conscious being is involved, say the station-master, and if he never changes his standpoint, then the facts known to him about the rays of light meeting at a point which seemed different from the one suggested by apparatus on the train, would never have led him to the idea that two different space-times were in operation here.   He would have combined the records of all the instruments within his own system of reference.   Only if the observer changes his standpoint, if the station-master gets on to the train, or if two persons are involved, do you have two opposed but equally warranted interpretations of the event.   The same thing is true in the hypothetical experiment with the box, or with the rotating disc, which suggest the equivalence of inertia and gravity.   All that we observe directly, or establish as necessary by experiment, are directions and velocities, which qualify the movement of objects in the box relative to its walls.   The two interpretations arise in so far as a conscious being takes up two different points of view, one after another, and discovers two contradictory interpretations of one and the same event.   It is only when we hold these two things apart quite clearly, the observed facts and the interpretation they will bear, that we are in the right position to assess the final consequences drawn in general relativity theory about the equivalence of inertia and gravitation, consequences which in this context we are able merely to indicate.   What is at issue is the explanation of gravitation in terms of curvature of the space-time continuum, and thus the hypothesis that a gravitational field is identical with a space-time curvature which obtains at the point in question. But, here, one of the functions of matter is involved.   It is the thesis that there is an equivalence relation between gravitation and inertia effects, which opened the way for this bold hypothesis. As a result, weight has lost its peculiar status. The theory has become untenable that there is a mysterious invisible attractive force exerted by bodies on other bodies, as Newton postulated. This force, combined with centrifugal forces, served to explain the elliptical orbits of the planets in their motion round the sun. If all this speculative theory be abandoned, and the planetary orbits are studied without prejudice, then it is possible to offer a quite different explanation of such curved tracks. There is no need to assume any special force which acts on the planets. The curved tracks have their origin in space-time itself. This, of course, requires that spaces other than Euclidean space come into the reckoning; spaces which, in relation to Euclidean space, are curved. Thus heavy bodies like the sun or the earth may conceivably produce a curvature in the space within their neighbourhood. Within such a curved continuum, the shortest distance between two points would not be, as in Euclidean space, a straight line, but a curved one. The planets, therefore, simply follow the shortest world-lines available to them in curved space. Jeans offers a simple illustration of the relation between the two explanations of the planetary orbits: that offered by Newton, and that offered by relativity. He compares a map of the earth drawn according to Mercator's projection, where lines of latitude and longitude are projected on to a flat surface, with a globe on which the same lines are curved. Think of a ship which is travelling by the quickest route from a British to an American port. If the track of the ship is plotted on a Mercator map, it will show a marked curvature, and may suggest to us that there must be forces acting upon the ship from the poles and deflecting it from the direct path. But if we take a globe, and stretch a piece of thread between the points marking the two ports, and pull the thread tight so that it marks the shortest path, we shall find that it indicates the route actually followed by the ship. Newton's theory of gravitation, says Jeans, explains the curved tracks of planets and comets in the same way as a passenger using a Mercator chart comes to suppose that the ship he is travelling on has been deflected from its direct course by an attractive force emanating from the poles. General relativity theory uses the globe, the curved space-continuum, to demonstrate what is happening. By reference to this, the complicated paths of the stars become the shortest paths, and no special force has to be introduced in order to explain them. This illustration of a globe and a Mercator map is naturally no more than an illustrative parable. For what is curved is not our perceptual space, but the four-dimensional continuum in which space and time are welded together into a 'union'. Thus, when it is said that within the world there are various 'regions of curvature', this is to be understood only in the sense of a visual image. So are the statements that in the neighbourhood of heavy bodies space develops a 'bulge' or 'buckle', or that reference systems produce 'reference-molluscs'.

To understand these final audacious conclusions of general relativity theory it is again important to note one thing which affects, not the observations of experimental physics, nor the calculations of theoretical physics, but rather the interpretation of their results in relation to a world-view. When general relativity theory talks about curved spaces, and when it combines space-time with matter in an inseparable unity, the impression may be given that it accepts the space-time continuum as an invisible material fluid which surrounds cosmic bodies and is curved under their influence, so that relativity theory, at this last stage of its development, has returned to the old ether-hypothesis. But this impression arises only because the physicists have tried to present to us a state of affairs which can only be represented mathematically, by means of parables which use material images, in order to bring it within range of our understanding. These images tend to be misleading, however, if we forget that they are only parables. The map and the globe used by Jeans to illustrate the curvature of space are both material images belonging to the Euclidean space of our perception. The point of departure, from which everything opens up, only *seems* to be brought within closer range of our understanding by the comparison of map and globe. What needs to be made comprehensible is the fact that the same line can be a curved line in one space, and therefore a roundabout way from one point to another,

and yet in another space be the 'shortest way' from one place
to another.   When I stretch a tight thread across the globe,
between the two points marking the ports, it is inside the
Euclidean space to which the globe belongs just as much as
does the map, and within that space it is not the shortest
connection between the two points, but the arc of a sector.
The shortest line would not pass outside across the surface
of the globe, but directly through the globe.   All lines and
figures on a spherical surface belong to Euclidean space as
much as do lines on a flat surface.   Spherical trigonometry
may work with spherical triangles, the sum of whose angles
is greater than two right-angles, but it does not at any point
take us outside the three-dimensional continuum and its
measurement relationships.   The sphere whose surface it is
describing belongs to Euclidean space just as does a plane
surface.   All these pictures, therefore, taken from the space
of our perception, provide no answer to the question: How
can it be that a line which in one space is a curve, and therefore a roundabout way from A to B, represents the most direct
connection between A and B in another space?   If we wish
to understand this, then it is not enough simply to consider
the objective facts.   Just as happened with the fundamental
experiments with the train or the box, so here we must include
within our scope the conscious being who interprets the facts
from his own standpoint.   Thus we give a meaning to the
results of relativity theory other than that suggested by many
modern physicists, its basis being found in Kantian philosophy.   According to Kant, an object is never there as such,
within the phenomenal world with which we are dealing all
the time in our experience and our natural science.   It is
there only as a subject's object of perception, which he sees
in the forms of his perception, and which he includes within
the categories of his understanding.   Therefore, from the
very outset we must take the conscious being into the range
of our consideration.   We may then conceive of a conscious
being whose realm of being is what we take to be a two-
dimensional surface.   All his perception is confined within
this realm, which is therefore the complex within which all
his experience must necessarily be fitted.   He is irrevocably

enclosed within it as in an eternal prison, just as we, with all our powers of perception, are imprisoned within three-dimensional space. For although we are in a position today, particularly since Riemann's fundamental work, to rise in *thought* above Euclidean space, with the help of mathematical formulae, and are able to construct the measurement relationships in spaces of any number of dimensions, our faculties of intuition and representation are limited, exactly as were those of Euclid and Newton, to three-dimensional space. With the best will in the world, we cannot conceive of four or more straight lines being at right angles to one another. We cannot therefore transport ourselves into a space of higher dimensionality than our own, i.e. of more than three dimensions. It is true that we can think ourselves into a space which has fewer dimensions than our own, and therefore into the world of a flat being, whose entire realm of existence consists in a two-dimensional surface. From that point, we are able to take a further step, and in the same way think ourselves into the situation of a surface-being whose realm of existence is not a plane surface, but one which to us has the curvature of the surface of a sphere. But such a being lacks the consciousness whereby to conceive of itself as existing on the surface of a sphere, that is to say in a space with a certain radius of curvature. It is a surface-being in just the same way as is the being whose realm of existence is a flat surface. A sphere, in our sense, is as inconceivable to such a being as is a co-ordinate system where four lines are mutually perpendicular to us. Therefore, for such a being, the arc made by the thread stretched between the two ports on the globe would in fact be the shortest conceivable connection between the two points. A spherical triangle, whose angles add up to more than two right angles, would be the only conceivable kind of triangle. If these two surface-beings, which live in different surfaces, were both mathematicians, they would necessarily see the same reality in different forms of spatial perception, but they would both be able, *in thought,* to rise above the perceptions appropriate to each of them. The mathematician of the flat surface would recognize the spherical surface to which his fellow mathematician is tied as a picture of the equation $x^2 + y^2 + z^2 = r^2$. The mathematician on the spherical surface would equally be able to represent the flat surface by an equation of the first degree, $ax + by + cz = d$. Of course the curved spaces which are discussed in general relativity theory are not simply two-dimensional surfaces which are curved in relation to one another like a plane and the surface of a sphere. They are space-time continua in the Minkowski sense, which have different radii of curvature in relation to one another. However, they stand in the same relation to one another, though with a much more complicated mathematical form, as do the spaces of the mathematician of the flat surface and the mathematician of the spherical surface. And in these relationships of higher dimensionality, the same situation fundamentally obtains between two mathematicians who exist in the different spaces. Each mathematician can represent the space in which the other lives by means of equations. But neither can see beyond the walls of the prison where he is confined, and look into the space of the other. Insurmountable limits have been set on either side to the possibilities of perceptibility. If these limits are to be transcended, it must be by thought-structures of a completely non-perceptive kind, which serve only to make it clear to either party that the space in which the other lives is *thinkable*. Nevertheless, these abstract constructions are not airy apparitions unrelated to reality. They have an immense significance for the understanding of this reality in which we exist. This is clear enough if we think in terms of the surface-being for whom three-dimensional space with its Euclidean measures is something utterly inconceivable, but who is able to construct it as an abstract possibility by mathematical formulae, provided he has the mathematical equipment. But for Euclidean beings like us, this three-dimensional space is the most living reality; it is the perceptible world in which we are bound to see everything that is given us to see. There may then be beings for whom another kind of space, of higher dimensionality, is just as perceptible as is the three-dimensional continuum to us, while for us that space is only a mathematically thought possibility. The mathematical formulae through which we represent other kinds of space are therefore not abstractions remote from reality, but meaningful symbols which make us aware of the immeasurable richness of the reality in which we exist. For they show us that this reality is mirrored in diverse spaces. The measurement relationships which obtain within these diverse spaces can be put in terms of one another, because there are constants which over-ride the disparity between the various spaces, and bring all thinkable spaces into a higher unity.

Now, at last, once the conscious being has been brought into the picture, the notion of 'curved space', which many people reject as suggesting an unintelligible 'crookedness of space', acquires an intelligible meaning. The term 'space-curvature' cannot mean that the space in which we live is a structure within which we might be able to detect a curvature, by using most delicate instruments to take measurements on a vast material surface. If one were able to detect any deviation from a level surface in such a plane, this would simply mean that a material structure within space happens to be curved, not that space itself exhibits curvature. To establish the fact of curvature at all, we should have to use an instrument such as a ruler or a measuring tape, whose straightness must be assumed. But any such instrument would itself be derived from our Euclidean space. Unless the procedure is to be circular, the non-curvature of this space must be established at the outset. Therefore we cannot, by the nature of the case, establish that space itself, rather than a material structure within it, is curved, by any geometrical means adopted within that space. It is now possible, however, to establish this physically.[1] This means that the curvature is not to be regarded as an attribute possessed by space when regarded geometrically and simply in itself. It refers always to the relation in which two or more spaces stand to one another, where the same reality is viewed from within each of them. In two spaces which are brought into such a relation with one another, the points which constitute the reality have a different order and arrangement. The spaces are so related that the lines marking in each of them the shortest distance

---

[1] The author is aware that this statement is disputed. Cf. p. 99.

between two points are curved in respect of one another. Seen from space A, the shortest possible path in space B between the two points is a curved line. Similarly, seen from space B, the most direct connection between the points in space A appears to be a curved line. This mutual relation between the two spaces becomes apparent only to a being who overlaps both spaces, and who, because he spans them both, is therefore in a position to see them both together and to grasp their mutual relation. In a previous volume it was maintained that there are such overlapping, more comprehensive, spaces, and that simpler spaces are contained within them as 'partial spaces', which have 'dimensional participation' in them. In this sense the two spaces of which we have spoken, namely the two-dimensional flat surface corresponding to the Mercator map, and the curved surface corresponding to the surface of the globe, are partial spaces of three-dimensional space, within which we are able to see them both at once. It is only because we are three-dimensional beings who live in a space to which both the two-dimensional spaces are related as partial spaces that we are capable of the comprehensive view which is denied to the two surface-beings whose spaces we are comparing with each other. For this reason alone are we in a position, not merely to formulate mathematically the relation between the two flat spaces, but also to make it a matter of genuine observation or perceptibility on our part. We can compare the Mercator map and the globe with each other. The spaces whose mutual relation is in question when space-curvature is mentioned in general relativity theory, are not, however, simply elementary surface spaces, but four-dimensional continua which include a dimension of time. Their mutual relationship could therefore only be grasped intuitively by a being who lives in a space of more dimensions than is the case with us. But why should there not be a consciousness which is more embracing, and which is able to span the difference of the spaces in which we are enclosed; a mind which exists in a space of which all our four-dimensional continua are but partial spaces, and which therefore is able to bring their mutual relations into view as a matter to be observed in the same way as we are able to observe the difference between a Mercator map and a globe?

11. PRACTICAL CONCLUSION

We can now formulate the conclusion to which we are led by these fundamental considerations, in order to sum up their effect. In general relativity theory, as we saw, both the demolition of the old objectivity and the construction of the new objectivity are carried through to final completion. These tasks began with the Copernican Revolution, and were taken up afresh by special relativity theory. In general relativity theory, the space-time systems which arise within different reference systems are relativized and turned into world-aspects belonging to subjects who see reality under different perspectives. By a further step, this procedure is extended to cover all spaces within which we are able to observe events from different points of perspective. Such spaces, understood in the sense of Kantian philosophy, become forms of intuition which are potentially contained in reality as objective possibilities. In this sense, these spatio-temporal forms of intuition are inseparable from matter. They can only be realized, however, when conscious beings are present, living in particular spaces.[1] This means that the last remnant of Ptolemaic objectivity, which lingered on in Newton's absolute space-time, has now been laid in ruins. But on these ruins there arises a more deeply rooted objectivity. We see that there is a Real not only on the further side of the various reference systems but also beyond the contrast of possible spaces, and we see it not merely in the fact that any system can be translated into terms of another, but also in the fact that the spaces stand in an exact mathematical relationship to one another, a fact we express symbolically when we talk of space-curvature, or of reference systems as reference molluscs.

But now, what is this Real, which stands beyond the con-

---

[1] These beings are able to choose their reference system, and to work within a chosen system. A satisfactory demonstration has been offered that, even in general relativity theory, a common world-time can be selected for the whole of the known stellar universe (Tolman).

trast of systems and spaces, and which expresses itself in different languages and is observed in different forms in all the spaces and reference systems? To this question we can only reply, with A. Wenzl: it is the potentiality which actualizes itself in different spatio-temporal world-pictures according to the choice of space and of reference system; world-pictures which can be translated into terms of one another. It is therefore the possibility which realizes itself in all this infinite variety of world-aspects. It is the unperceived x which carries within its womb all the cine-films of the world-process which it is possible to produce from different standpoints. These possibilities, however, are only actualized when particular reference systems are given by which conscious beings are related to reality. Thus we have traced back the world's secret, as did Aristotelian philosophy, to the relation of *actus* and *potentia,* actuality and possibility. The ultimate reality, the goal to which all roads lead, is a fruitful womb from which are born all the world-pictures which come into the light of consciousness. Here we can bring in a further point which serves to light up another aspect of the matter. In the Minkowski world, as we saw, things have been transformed into events which proceed along their world-lines. Now there is no uniformly flowing stream of time, and no absolute simultaneity. Within different systems, time has a different rate. The world as it is in itself, seen, that is to say, in abstraction from any selected reference system, has therefore no definite 'temporality' throughout. It simply *is.* It is a multiplicity of points which only begin to form stretches of time among themselves when a reference system is provided. Reality, considered in abstraction from all conscious beings, is therefore timeless. It is something eternal which becomes time only by the provision of particular systems. In this eternal thing, the distinction between past, present and future is not yet to be found. Everything that develops and unfolds itself in time through a slower or faster sequence of events for limited beings like us, is a single *nunc aeternum* within this eternal being.

Having acknowledged this, physics has come to the point where, for the second time, it stands at the frontier across which lies the 'inner space', the realm which can no longer be objectified, to which we ourselves belong in our deepest essence. For the new objectivity, which has arisen phoenix-like from the collapse of the old Ptolemaic world-structure, is something completely beyond perceptibility and representation. If we hope to get an inner grasp on this Real which stands above the diversity of all spaces and systems and contains in itself all potentialities, then two possibilities are open for us. Either we may rest content with the abstract structure of thought which describes, in the language of mathematical equations, the relations between the spatio-temporal pictures which reflect the unrepresentable basic reality, much as the sun is reflected in raindrops through a million new angles of refraction so that in the rainbow we are able in fact to see the sun in spite of the fact that it is something we cannot look at without being blinded. In this case, where we rest content with such mathematical formulae, we have stopped at the frontier set for objective thinking and purely scientific enquiry. Or else we cross the frontier. And this is possible only because our knowledge is not confined to the objective world which surrounds us on all sides and with which alone physical thinking is equipped to deal. We also know ourselves. Each of us knows that he is not merely standing in objective space, but at the same time he exists in a realm to which the self belongs but which is not perceptible. I am aware of my own existence. This awareness belongs to my existence. I am 'thrown into my thereness' (*geworfen in mein Da*), as Heidegger says. I am confined to this position in space which is my home, thrown into my Now which is the point of time that I call 'my' time, confined to this body whose destiny is 'my' destiny. But the necessity with which I am thus thrown into this position is neither logically conditioned nor causally conditioned. It is unconditioned, and therefore irrevocable. The riddle of my existence is bound up with this necessity. I can either run away from this riddle of my existence, and try to merge into objectivity, or I must stand and face the burning question posed by my existence as to the source of this particular placing. What this placing of our existence means has become fully clear for

the first time through relativity theory. Along with my existence, there is conferred on me an origin of co-ordinates within the space to which I belong, a world-centre, a point of
perspective, from which particular measurements of space or
time or motion hold good. I have not chosen this reference
system for myself. It has been allotted to me. In the course
of my life I can, of course, keep on changing my position. In
thought or imagination also I can move to another point in
the world. But all these changes of position, whether achieved
in thought or in reality, have a constant point of origin, and
can never carry me entirely out of range of that point. This
is the original reference system in which I found myself at
my entrance into existence. This world-centre is the original
point of departure for my cosmic orientation. It is my
original home, to which I am always attracted back. And it
is not a home of my choice which I have sought out for myself.
It is my destiny.

General relativity theory also shows us that this reference
system in which originally I find myself to be is within a
space of a definite dimensional structure, which has a definite
relation of curvature to other spaces. It is by no free decision
of our own that we live in Euclidean space, and therefore can
only think in terms of three-dimensional pictures and must
fall back upon mathematics to express spaces of higher dimensions. We have not chosen this space. It is our destiny to be
Euclidean beings. This has been decided about us without
our having any say in the matter.

What is the origin of this irrevocable decision which assigns
to us such a world-centre and a space? The point from which
the decision proceeds must lie beyond the conflict of all the
systems and all the spaces. For if it were to lie within any
system or space, it would itself presuppose the 'placing' of a
space and a system. It would itself rest upon yet another
decision in virtue of which that system had been established.
Therefore it would not be the ultimate origin from which
all systems proceed. Only at a point which itself is outside
all the differences of systems and spaces can the decision be
taken about which of all the possible systems should be
assigned to you or to me as our realm of existence. The power

which makes this decision must therefore sustain potentially within itself the entire world-process, and all the forms in which it may be presented. The power which assigns this place to me as my 'here', must itself transcend every here or there and every possible local difference, and therefore must be omnipresent. The power which assigns this moment to me, as my 'now', must itself transcend past, present and future. It must sustain within itself, as *nunc aeternum,* the entire course of time from which every system takes its own peculiar time scale. It must therefore be eternal.

It thus appears that, if we do not evade the riddle presented to us by our own existence, we are led to the same point which scientific knowledge reaches when pursued to its ultimate consequences. Existential reflection and physical research, though arising from opposite poles, intersect at one and the same point. The potentiality which is able to actualize itself in the vast range of mathematically related systems, and the non-temporal regulative source which permits of development into the different time scales, are to us further manifestations of the omnipotence, omnipresence and eternity of the world-ground from which our own personal existence proceeds. The super-spatial and super-temporal potentiality of this world-ground lies beyond the range of our intuition. For only that which can be regarded in our own space from within a definite reference system falls within the range of intuition. The possibility which lies beyond all such space is not only invisible to us, but also beyond all power of representation. The Original Power to which we owe our existence 'dwelleth in light unapproachable'.

Is this all that can be said about this original ground which contains in its womb all forms of existence, and all destinies of life, as possibilities? Because this world-ground is beyond intuition or representation, it is therefore open to us to rest content in our ignorance and to say that this maternal womb of all events is an impersonal X which, like the wave of some mighty sea, has thrown us up with inexorable necessity on to the shore of this world. We must therefore accept with resignation this boundary-notion to which physics has led us. If we stop at this point, we have indeed given expression to the final knowledge which is attainable within objective space. But this objective space is not the whole of the reality which lies open before us. If we consider this space in and for itself, we have postulated a kind of aesthetic isolation. We live in an abstraction. We have overlooked something which has the necessary connection with the whole of reality as has the key in which a tune is written to the tune itself, or as the shape of a coloured surface has to the reality of the surface. We have put brackets round our own existence, which, though indeed it cannot be objectified, is nevertheless something in which we are inescapably fixed. If I rest content with the impersonal X to which physical research leads me, and simply talk about an 'original ground', an 'original womb', or 'an original source' of all being and all events, I am in fact evading the burning question posed by my own existence of which I am made aware in all seriousness when, to quote Heidegger, in the face of the threat of death I am called back to myself, called away from my anonymity in the public life and chatter of impersonal 'man', which is where I took refuge from the horror of that despair into which I am cast; and now, bereft of the home and hiding place which 'man' in general afforded me, I must quietly accept myself and the whole horror of my solitary existence. Only if that happens am I wakened from the lost dream-state in which hitherto I have been living, and I come to myself. In these circumstances it becomes alarmingly clear to me that all the neutral, impersonal words which are produced today in such variety as solutions for the riddle of life—words such as destiny, fate, ἀνάγκη, *Urd*—are indeed justified as provisional expressions of the unsolved riddle which my existence carries with it, or of the burning question which cries to be answered as soon as I have renounced the flight from myself. But they are not solutions of the riddle, nor answers to the question. The words εἱμαρμένη, ἀνάγκη appeared in Greek tragedy with Aeschylus and Sophocles at a time when the ancient religious faith of Greece was being destroyed and the question about life's meaning first arose and threatened the Greeks with all the force of the riddle of the Sphinx. The same is true of the old German word *Urd* which means so much. Our Germanic ancestors groped for this word at the time when the old gods were declining. They used it to acknowledge that they stood in the presence of a dark original power fraught with disaster, which hung over their lives like a black thunder-cloud, but whose power exceeded all understanding. All such impersonal fate-words are an expression of resignation by which all hope of an answer to the question about life's meaning is deliberately renounced, and men close their eyes to everything but the universal causal nexus where the destiny of their own lives is bound up with the totality of life. If we divest these words of the mysterious nimbus in which they are veiled and hold on simply to their plain meaning, there can be no doubt but that these words refer to nothing else but the inevitable causal nexus within which stands the entire psycho-somatic life of men. Human life, both in its bodily and in its psychic aspects, is the product of a scale of inheritance, which we receive in accordance with biological laws. This received inheritance is developed in new forms and structures through an untold range of historical events and under the many influences of a parental home, education, environment and the passage of time. A human individual may therefore be compared to the leaf on the widely spreading tree of 'the people', a leaf produced in spring by the rising sap in the main trunk, a leaf which unfolds under the influence of sun and rain, and which finally is whipped from its twig and blown away by the autumn gales. It is this range of efficient causes, this inexorable causal nexus in which we are immersed and to which every individual life is subject, which is summed up in the impersonal notion of fate.

But, in view of what has been said, it is clear that the burning question posed by my personal existence has not yet been raised if nothing save the causal nexus in which every human life is set comes under consideration. It is not the impression of a causal nexus to which the life-story of every man is subject which gives rise to this question. We shall have more to say about this causal nexus in a subsequent section. The riddle of my existence emerges primarily out of the mysterious fact that to me alone, out of all the myriad forms of life which have inhabited this earth for millions of years and will go on inhabiting it, should be allotted this psycho-somatic structure as the place to which I am inexorably bound. To be thus bound, as we saw, is something whose root lies beyond the objective causal nexus. The various levels of causal explanation of the world would not be affected in the least if another place and another time had been allotted to me as my seat of action. The decision by which I am placed within the world of experience at this precise place in unalterable relationship to it is one lying completely outside the whole objective sphere. It lies in an entirely different dimension. It belongs to non-objective space. Therefore if I suppose that I have done something towards solving the riddle of my existence when I use impersonal words like destiny and fate, then either I have not seen the great question mark which hangs over my existence, or I am deliberately avoiding the question, or I am mistaken about its solution. I have confused myself with an object such as those which stand over against me, that is to say with an element in the objective world, to which indeed I stand in a given relationship, but which I can always distinguish clearly from my own self. I have confused my 'I' with an 'It' which stands in the objective causal nexus. It is this confusion which comes to expression when I use impersonal words like fate or destiny in order to explain my existence, words which explicitly have an 'It' character, and belong within the category of objectivity.

At the peak of the Idealistic period in German thought, Fichte rediscovered the non-objective 'I' in its complete independence of all objective world-connections, and saw, in opposition to all destiny-myths, that this 'I' stands beyond the whole of objective space. Every objective event, including the rise and fall of solar systems as well as the emergence and destruction of the body which I call my own, can for me be nothing more than a stage-play, according to Fichte. I cannot therefore have originated from any 'It', and neither shall I be destroyed by any 'It'. When this conviction broke triumphantly through once again into German thought, like the sun through the clouds, then Greek and old German fate-myths faded away. The 'I' cannot have received its existence from the hand of an 'It'. It cannot have been thrown on to the shore of this world by a blind wave of fate. It can only have been put here by an 'I'. There are thus two possible explanations of it. The first is the one which Fichte himself adopted for a time, namely that I have put myself here, and continue every moment to posit myself afresh. The other possibility is the biblical conviction that I have not put myself here, but have been set here by an eternal 'Thou', which is not identical with myself and never can be, but which stands over against me to all eternity. I have to decide as between these two intuitions. There is no third possibility. The fatalistic explanation of the 'I' in terms of the 'It' is ruled out. Further, the agnosticism into which I can retreat seems to me to be a vain attempt to flee from the question which is bound up with my existence, once I am thoroughly alive to its reality. Humanity is tossed to and fro between the two possibilities which remain, once it is realized that the way of the fate-myth and the way of flight into the Night of Unknowing are both blocked. The first possibility means that I will venture upon the titanic claim that I have posited myself and that I go on doing so from moment to moment. But I must follow this through to its logical end. This means that I myself am the unconditioned absolute 'I', the original power which lies beyond all spaces and reference systems and carries in its womb all possibilities of existence. I am the world's creator, and my spatially limited human existence is the product of a self-limitation which I have myself undertaken by means of a free sovereign decision. It is myself as absolute 'I' which marks off myself as relative 'I' from all relative 'not-I'. This is a notion of which man is only capable in the smoke of some demonic self-divinization. If the sober reality of my limited being prevents such a flight to the sun, and, like Icarus, I drop back with singed wings to the ground of reality, I then realize that this titanic self-divinization was in fact a boundless solipsism which I could not for long endure, and from which there could be no deliverance except by the second possibility enshrined in the biblical conviction that I have not put myself here, but have been put here. But such a placing, in virtue of which I am, cannot be the work of any impersonal power. The 'I' cannot be posited through an 'It'. If I have not come to be here through myself, then it is only through a 'Thou' that I have been put here, the eternal 'Thou' who stands beyond all spaces, and upon whom I unconditionally depend. Through this eternal 'Thou', with whom I can never be identical in all eternity, I am delivered from my desperate loneliness. I am not alone, for I live always in the presence of this Other. But this Other, who has made me and given me to myself, has a claim on my whole life. I am responsible to Him for all that I have made of my life. For it is to Him that I owe my whole existence.

Natural science has no bearing on the choice between these two basic intuitions which have been in conflict throughout the history of thought. The decision takes place in the inner realm of personal life, and it is not by my power that it happens. Only the living God Himself can take away the bandage round my eyes by meeting me personally and giving me the certainty that I have received my life from His hands, and that He has entrusted it to me like a pound with which to trade until such time as He calls me to account for it. But when the miracle happens to me, by which the man born blind is able to see, then the whole development which began with the Ptolemaic world-picture and ends with the general relativity theory takes on a new aspect. What has come under review in this section is nothing more nor less than the history of all the attempts man has made to posit for himself, in titanic fashion, the Absolute which he needs. On the one hand he raised to the status of the Absolute an element in the objective world around him. Thus by his own decision he found an absolute point of rest, absolute motion, absolute space, absolute time, an absolute reference body and absolute space-time scales. On the other hand, when these objective absolutes began to collapse, he made the bold resolve to posit himself as the absolute foundation without which he could not be alive. All these world-structures, whether supplied from the external world or built on self-posited absolutes, have collapsed one after another. Their foundations have been shown to be relative. They were all therefore built on sand. But the collapse of all such self-imposed constructions of the human mind has been only the negative preparation for a final acknowledgment of a remarkably positive character. God, the Creator, who stands as the Eternal beyond all our systems, is the sole Absolute. We trace the power of those unconditional decisions which He alone is able to make in the irrevocable 'placing' which has allocated to us our place in space and time. In all the change of appearances, our eternal point of rest is in God alone. In the whole created world there are only relative magnitudes and relative scales. If the creature were to tear itself loose from the Creator, it would find itself abandoned to a chaos of mere relative pictures and arbitrary locations, and all its foundations would begin to tremble. The creature finds an absolute mid-point, an eternal centre of rest, only when it turns again into community with the Creator. For the creature depends on the Creator, and is ordered entirely in relation to Him.

IV

ABSOLUTE DETERMINISM
IN NATURAL EVENTS AND THE
A-CAUSAL CONCEPT USED
IN MODERN PHYSICS

12. THE CONCEPT OF CAUSAL NECESSITY

We have been occupied with two absolutes upon which men have built their world-structures, first the absolute object which is independent of all subjects, and secondly absolute space and absolute time surrounding us on all sides like a house in which we live safely. Both these absolutes have been called into question by recent physics. In the first place, the absolute object lost its status as absolute when it appeared that two mutually complementary pictures of the same object arose at the same point, varying in accordance with the condition of the subject and his means of observation, and that these two pictures could not be held together in one moment of intuition but could be related to one another only by means of non-intuitive mathematical formulae. In the second place, absolute space and absolute time, which Newton believed in, lost their status as absolute when it was proved that spatio-temporal measurements were conditional on the state of motion of the observer.

In this new section, we shall be dealing with a third absolute which, from a practical point of view, is even more important than the two we have been considering. I mean the absolute determination by causal law of all that happens. In the case of the absolute object, or of the absolute spatio-temporal structure, what was involved was something which continued in the same unalterable condition. But the thing which gives to our existence its peculiar character, and which so far has not come under scrutiny, is the fact that we, together with the whole world to which we belong, are not in a fixed static condition nor in some immutable state, but rather that we are in a constant state of transformation; for each moment that which so far has been the present sinks back into being obstinately past and something new dominates the scene in its place. This unbroken sequence of forward-moving events, which gives to our life a duration in which we never come to rest, is the thing to which our attention is drawn when we talk about cause and effect, ground and consequence, a rigid causal nexus, predetermination of the future; or when we say 'that is bound to happen', or 'this will have far-reaching consequences', or 'the curse of an evil action is that it must breed more evil'.

The causal law of which such words remind us is, in the first instance, a summary of previous experience. It expresses the rule by which events have hitherto followed upon one another and conditioned one another. But if this is how the sense of causal happening is produced, then this law has only theoretical significance in the theory of knowledge. It gives no directives for the future which are of use in natural science, particularly in technical science and medicine. What we need is some certainty about the rules which govern the future into which we are bound to advance at every moment. For it is part of our destiny that a veil hangs over the future towards which we are progressing. No man is lord of the future. We must, from the outset, be explicitly aware of this decisive and important situation. Only so shall we understand the immense practical significance of the causal principle. We are trying to lay hold on some fact which sheds light on the relation in which we stand to the future. Visitors to the Krupp works used to be shown a steam-hammer which came down with tremendous force when a certain knob was pressed and was guaranteed to flatten any object placed beneath it. The mechanism which controlled the hammer was so arranged that the man in charge could stop the descent of the hammer at any point he chose. You could therefore put a glass tumbler or a wrist-watch on the platform, and adjust the working of the hammer to take account of the height of the object in question. The hammer came down with all its force, but stopped at just the right distance above the platform, and the object lying there was untouched. Every visitor who saw this amazing machine and what could be done with it was quite persuaded that the man in charge of it had complete control over the crushing power which it exhibited every time it descended. What was so interesting however was the reaction of the visitors when the engineer said: 'Now see for yourselves whether I am right. Put your hand on the platform, and we will have a practical demonstration that the machine works properly, and that nothing can happen except what is decreed by the way I adjust the mechanism.' What was the response to this challenge? Not a single visitor dared to take up the challenge and to make the dangerous test. All of them were of the opinion that nothing would go wrong. What was it then which prompted the slight shudder they felt at the prospect of putting their own hands under the hammer? It was not that they lacked confidence in the reliability of the machine or of the man in charge. No, the real ground of their uncertainty, their hesitation and their slight shudder lay simply and solely in this, that the event which mattered here was not in the past where everything is firmly established and where the reliability of the whole mechanical contraption had been abundantly proved, but that it lay still in the future. The episode is interesting because it sheds a lurid light on what is involved in every instance of a transition from a past to a future event. It reminds us of the chasm which exists between our consciousness of what has already happened and our consciousness of things which still lie in the future. With every step into the dark future we have to put our hand on the platform in an uncertainty which is greater or less according to circumstances. 'The past is eternally still.' We can find repose in it. But everything that is future, even if it is to be expected in accordance with well-known and frequently attested physical laws such as enable us to predict an eclipse, even if it is quite simply bound to happen, can never be absolutely certain. Always it is only possible, potential, in the best cases probable, perhaps very probable, but never absolutely certain. This is something to be recognized whenever we commit ourselves without reserve to a law which has always been valid according to the causal-mechanical world-picture.

To reach the right starting point from which to shape our attitude to this question about the determination of the future, we must begin from this clear and inviolable frontier which separates the whole of what is in the perfect tense from the whole of what is in the future. There are two possibilities in regard to what is future, and they produce different impressions of the state of the case. The future can be the object of pre-vision of a clairvoyant or prophetic kind. Such pre-vision is entirely independent of human volition or planning. Clairvoyant pre-vision, second sight for instance, is connected with sense-perception and is often mistaken for it inasmuch as it has the same form of material sensation, especially when it comes in the form of dreams. Frederick the Great's valet, for instance, reports this experience: 'One night, some years after the Seven Years War, I heard the king cry out: "Fire!   Fire! " I rushed into his bedroom, but nothing was burning. The king was lying on his bed, groaning heavily, and clearly disturbed by bad dreams. I took it upon myself to waken him. "Ach," he said, " it is good that you wakened me. I had a terrible dream. I dreamt that I was standing on the terrace of Sans-souci, and all around me I saw my country and my castles packed closely together, and behind them all I seemed to see the whole world with all its cities and countries. It all lay before me like a wonderful picture, and I was delighted by it. Suddenly the heavens grew dark, black clouds swept across the sky, deep night covered the fair world, uncanny screeches and groans filled the air. A blazing star flashed out from between the clouds and fell like lightning. The earth flared up in fire and smoke. The darkness was transformed into the brightness of day. The fire ate its way over ever-widening circles and burnt all my castles which crashed in ruins. The fallen star had consumed them all and burnt my whole territory. It turned the rivers into blood-red streams and the corn-fields into waste land. And when I looked beyond my own lands, I saw how the star had crashed like a rocket upon all the other countries of the earth, spreading fire everywhere, until all lands and all cities were reduced to ashes. Then I shouted Fire! And you wakened me."

'The king went on to say: "This dream has a meaning, and something most remarkable has certainly happened to-night. Write down exactly what I have said, and note the date and the year." It was in fact August 15th, 1769, at three o'clock in the morning—the hour of Napoleon's birth.'

No one can fully gauge the significance of that particular hour when, to an hitherto utterly unknown family in Corsica, a son was born. Nor can we give a final historical verdict about his significance. But in every experience of this kind we see the reality of clairvoyant powers.

The other kind of relation with the future is completely different from such involuntary pre-vision. It is not a matter of pre-vision at all, but rather of prediction, based on con-clusions reached in a thoroughly rational way from events which belong to the perfect tense. Instances of this are weather forecasts or astronomical predictions. How do prog-noses of this kind come to be made? How do we perform the complicated intellectual process of drawing conclusions which make possible an anticipation in thought of future events? Here, obviously, we are dealing with the origin of the notion of causality; with the bold idea that there is a law of nature or a causal necessity which governs not merely the realm of the past but also the realm of the future; with a syllogism built out from the continent of the past into the mists of the future. As soon as we are fundamentally clear about the specific difference between past and future happenings, it is at once apparent that the notion of universal validity, which we had previously taken to apply not only to the past but also to the whole future, requires no further elucidation. It implies a leap across a chasm, a brave attempt to bridge the gulf which separates us from the other realm lying beyond the frontier of what has already happened. More than once in the history of astronomy it has happened that a star has been discovered by telescope, astronomers having predicted that it must be at that particular point of space. It is a matter of regular experience that an eclipse of the sun or the moon is predicted, and that it happens at the exact moment stated. Whenever such a prediction is successful, we enjoy the proud feeling that the human mind has made a successful leap into the dark, a leap which might easily have failed for one reason or another. Though this has happened thousands of times, we nevertheless feel pleased every time because man has won another victory over the darkness which tries to hide the future from our eyes. Pascual Jordan says that the peculiar triumph of science, which keeps on dropping like a gift into our lap, does not consist in its power to explain the riddle of the past, but rather in its power to predict in detail the results of a future experiment and the prediction is in fact fulfilled.

Starting from this situation, then, we address ourselves to the problem of causal necessity. In the last resort, the whole of philosophical speculation about causal necessity is a means by which men try to overcome the dread and uncertainty which they have about the future, whose roots are deep in our existence. Distinctions are made between moral necessity, logical necessity and physical necessity. Moral necessity is the sacred obligation with which the ethical imperative drives us forward. Logical necessity is the cogency exhibited in a simple syllogism: 'All men are mortal. Socrates is a man. Therefore he must die.' If we choose to put causal or physical necessity into line with logical or ethical necessity, then we should notice at once that this case is different from the other two. This kind of necessity is not directed to our wills, as is ethical necessity where we ourselves make some contribution to the accomplishment of the necessity. And the case is also different from that of logical necessity, for this rests on evidence which lights up for us the fact that 1 is 1 and a is a. All mathematical, and all logical conclusions rest on evidence of this kind. But the case is quite different with the necessity of causal-mechanical laws.

Here we are not dealing with what is already given and belongs to the past. We are dealing much more with the future. For it is clear that as long as we remain firmly on the ground of what is directly given to us, as long as we refuse to trespass beyond the sphere of our own pure experience, then Hume's positivist theory about the essence of causality is perfectly correct. The theory of causal necessity, according to Hume, arises like this. Our previous experience, namely the past, has shown over and over again that the same sequence of events could be observed in thousands of instances. Always the day has been followed by the night. Lightning (of the proper kind) has always been followed by thunder. When this has happened thousands of times, event B having always followed upon event A, then the force of custom provokes an involuntary expectation that the next time event A happens it will be followed by event B. Thus arises a theory of causal necessity. The causal principle itself is obviously not explained by this superficial explanation, but one thing is firmly established. The thing which is directly given as a secure and incontestable hypothesis and which afforded a starting point for the concept of a causal principle is the regular sequence of experiences in the region of former happenings from which we derive the involuntary expectation of repetition in the future. But the moment one attempts to derive a necessary consequence from this ever-repeated sequence of A and B, one goes beyond the competence of human experience by building out into the future a mental construct.

From this point we proceed to the new estimate which Kant offers. We have before us the monumental construction which he bequeathed to us, namely the transcendental deduction of the forms of intuition and of the categories of the understanding. The eternally unknown 'thing-in-itself' of world reality is 'affected' for the thinking subject. This unknown thing-in-itself converts itself into an experience, provided two *a priori* postulates are fulfilled. First, time and space must be given as the two forms of intuition without which nothing is able to confront us objectively. Secondly, categories of the understanding must be provided, in particular those of substance and causality. Through these alone can an intuited object become an object of thought. There is the *a priori* possibility of experience only when both exist simultaneously and in relation to one another. 'Concepts without intuitions are empty. Intuitions without concepts are blind.' Here it is not our intention to expound in detail the work done by Kant in the *Critique of Pure Reason* in respect of the transcendental deduction of the forms of intuition and the categories of the understanding. It is one of the most impressive achievements of the German mind. Here it is enough to pick out the one thing which matters in this context, namely that causal necessity appears as a category of the understanding, the central category indeed; not merely as a summary of past experience, but also as a postulate of all possible future experience. The human mind decrees the sovereign validity of the causal law for the entire future. In a previous section, the Transcendental Aesthetic, Kant had maintained the validity for all the future of one-dimensional time and three-dimensional Euclidean space. He did not, of course, want to dictate terms to Nature itself through such *a priori* postulates of all experience. Nature, as thing-in-itself, remains an unknown X, a veiled picture. What is decreed for all time by this dictate of philosophical thinking is the form in which alone men like ourselves are able to catch a glimpse of reality. That form is bound up with these postulates. In the meantime, however, the conclusions of philosophy have suffered a severe blow at the hands of scientific research. The dictates of the human mind in regard to forms of intuition have today been frustrated by modern physics. Euclidean geometry, in so far as it counts at all, has become an 'empirical science'. No longer is it an *a priori* prescription of all experience, but, on the contrary, the prescriptions of its own validity and of the limits within which it holds are derived from experience. This was the first of the blows which shook to its foundations the proud structure of the transcendental deduction of the *a priori* presuppositions of experience. It meant a reversal of the relation which had obtained between the human mind and Nature. This same reversal had to be extended to deal with the other parts of the Kantian structure, the categories of the understanding such as substance and causality. The same was true of these categories as of the forms of intuition. Modern physics is not prepared to take the risk of dictating to Nature about the validity of these categories, especially causality, as though they ought to hold for the future *a priori*, i.e. prior to all experience. The validity of the causal principle depends on the results of experimental observation. It is of the utmost significance for our whole attitude to Nature, and for our whole feeling about life, that some of our leading physicists regard the universal validity of the causal principle as far from obvious, and that they are prepared at least to reckon with the possibility that the law of causality which is found generally within the macroscopic realm no longer holds in the microscopic realm of Nature. For we are now aware that Kant's transcendental philosophy is not, as it had been taken to be, a secure theory resting on exact philosophical reflection. Rather is it a bold attempt on the part of the human mind to bridge the gulf which separates us from the unknown future, and to do so indeed by an unproved assumption that causal necessity in world happenings governs the future as well as the past. This assumption is not a result of observation, for the future is not yet open to observation; but neither is it a conclusion from the past, as Hume thought, for as such it would be merely an insecure hypothesis. Nor is it a mere postulate, for then the wish would merely be father to the thought. There is only one term we can apply to it, the highest and most heavily loaded term which we have. It is a *faith*, a faith in the same sense in which we called original materialism a religious faith. Just as faith in an absolute object or in eternal matter was a religious faith which stood opposed to faith in God and indeed ruled it out, so also faith in absolute determination or causal necessity of all future world happenings is a religious faith.

This faith, like any religious faith which is at grips with the dark future towards which man is always striding, holds on to something invisible and puts all its confidence in this invisible reality. We may recall once again the definition of faith given by Luther in the Large Catechism, which was meant to cover all forms of religious faith including heathen ones. When the men of this technical age entrust their lives to some technical device such as an aeroplane or a mountain railway, the invisible reality to which they commit themselves is the causal necessity by which a well-constructed machine is bound to move in terms of the physical laws according to which it has been built. Behind this, as the invisible object of faith, there is always the causal-mechanical world-picture envisaged by Laplace, resting on unalterable laws (notably the law of inertia, the law of gravitation and the laws of electro-physics), where nothing can happen that cannot be calculated in respect of any future time. This world-picture is the symbolical representation of the invisible reality in which technical man trusts with his whole heart. His whole existence has been built upon it, and therefore his entire behaviour can be orientated with respect to it. The religious character of this faith in causality becomes particularly clear in the case of Spinoza who, for the first time, identified God and causal necessity. For Spinoza, religion is nothing else but *amor fati*. It means for him an attempt to love with all our hearts the causal necessity under which we stand.

Theodore Lessing in *Geschichte als Sinngebung des Sinn-losen* (*History as Giving Meaning to the Meaningless*), a Nietzschean work written in 1919, suggested that 'approval of necessity' is the core of religion. We can trace the power of this great religious faith in the manner in which men who are filled with this faith stride into the dark future. In this faith there is a total repudiation of all attempts to establish a personal relationship with the power which presides over the future. Men who are serious about this faith and are threatened with death are utterly resolved to hold out to the last moment without praying, and courageously to resist all temptations to pray. Within this harsh and prayerless faith in the necessity of all that happens, two things are found side by side: first, a fatalistic dread of the irresistible fate which crushes us after long struggles; secondly, the peace which proceeds precisely from this hopelessness.

13. THE DEBATE ABOUT CAUSALITY WITHIN MODERN PHYSICS

A question which is of decisive importance for our world-outlook is under discussion within modern physics. Is physical happening something which, by its very structure, must be determined? Does it take place in a sequence comparable to that by which a pre-fabricated film unrolls? Or are alternative possibilities open all the time? Because this is a question on which a great deal depends, we must accept with extreme caution any provisional answers which affect our world-outlook, at any rate so long as the physicists continue their debate. This, however, means that what little can be regarded as settled is extremely important. It is precisely at this point that we can see most clearly the change which has come over natural science, in that it has moved from the causal-mechanical picture beloved of a technical age which believed in magnitudes fixed and absolute in themselves, to a mode of thought for which all these absolute fundamentals have been relativized. We have illustrated this change already with reference to questions about absolute space and absolute time, taken as the framework within which events occur. If it has been made clear that a change has happened in physical thought about these two questions, it should be even clearer that here, at this third decisive point which is now under consideration, there has been a decisive repudiation of the causal-mechanical world-picture which dominated the scene for so long. According to classical physics, matter was composed of corpuscles, simple indivisible elements which, since their extension was negligible, could be treated as points. These corpuscles existed in objective Euclidean space whose structure was completely transparent to our minds. Within this space they moved according to fixed laws, of inertia, gravitation and electro-physics, which could be formulated mathematically. On this supposition, the entire future development of the material world could be worked out, provided that at some given moment one knew the location, the charge and the momentum (mass × velocity) of each corpuscle. This was the situation in which Laplace was able to make his classical statement of universal determinism: 'If it were possible, at a given moment, to know all the forces by which nature is moved, and the situation of all the beings out of which it is composed, and if there were a mind sufficiently comprehensive to subject all these phenomena to the right analysis, then the movement of the largest bodies in the universe and of the smallest atoms could be included within one and the same formula. For such a mind, nothing would be uncertain any more, and the future, like the past, would be present before its sight.' Dubois Reymond, the Berlin physiologist, drew the further consequence from this: ' Just as an astronomer needs only to give a certain negative value to the time factor in the equations of the moon in order to determine whether the sun was eclipsed at the Piraeus when Pericles embarked for Epidaurus, so Laplace's " Mind" would be able to tell us, by manipulation of his world-formula, who the Iron Mask was, or how the *President* was wrecked. Just as an astronomer can predict the day when a comet will suddenly reappear in our skies after years of absence in the depths of the universe, so this " Mind" could read off from its equations the precise day on which the Greek Cross will cease to shine down from St. Sophia, or the day when England will burn its last lump of coal. If in his world-formula he put $t = -\infty$, the mysterious origin of all things would be unveiled for him.'

Nowadays the status of the corpuscles from which the world of classical physics was built, and the absolute monarchy of the objective universe, have both become problematic. Faith in the world-machine whose workings are inexorably determined has therefore been shattered. The destruction began in the penultimate stage of atomic research, when it was demonstrated from the work of Planck, Rutherford, Bohr and others that the ultimate constituents of reality are not individual indestructible corpuscles such as the all-embracing Laplace Mind needed for its calculations. Matter is constantly dissolving into changing forms of energy, and it can be said, with Jeans, that ' matter does not exist; it happens '.

The existence of Planck's action-quantum h was another nail in the coffin of the hypothesis which was Laplace's starting-point, namely that it was theoretically possible to know simultaneously the location and the momentum of a corpuscle. No process of observation and measurement is known by which the position of a corpuscle in space and its velocity can be accurately determined together. For any contrivance which serves to determine the position 'disturbs' the velocity, and does so the more radically as the technique for determining position becomes more exact. On the other hand, a contrivance designed to measure the velocity 'disturbs' the position, and the disturbance becomes worse the more accurately the velocity is measured. Heisenberg was the first to recognize and to give mathematical expression to this implication of quantum theory, in his 'Uncertainty Principle'. 'A particle can have a position or it can have a velocity, but in the strict sense it cannot have both. . . . Nature puts up with our probings into its mysteries only on conditions. The more we clarify the secret of position, the more deeply hidden becomes the secret of velocity. It reminds one of the man and woman in the weather house: if one comes out, the other goes in. . . . The product of the two unknowns is always an integral multiple of an elementary quantum of action. We can distribute the uncertainty as we wish, but we can never get away from it.'

The experts have tried, in their popular expositions, to make things clear in the following way, in order to offer some measure of interpretation of a fundamental law which is so difficult to understand.

We wish to determine the position of a particle. In order to do so, we must look at it. To be able to look at it, we must illuminate it, for we cannot see it in the dark. We must direct a ray of light upon it, and 'lay our sights' on it. There is no difficulty about this when we are dealing with macroscopic bodies which are large in comparison with the wavelength of light. It is as though a football were thrown at the earth. However hard the player bounces it, the earth itself is not disturbed. But if the particle which we must illuminate in order to see it should be as small as an electron, then the ray of light, the photon, which falls upon it evokes a reaction. This reaction is a certain fraction of the impulse of the photon. It is therefore only possible to observe the object on the hypothesis that whatever is observed will be altered. The psychologist meets the same difficulty when he wants to investigate the motions of his own soul. For instance, if I want to observe in myself the mental action of going to sleep, then the action itself is disturbed and indeed rendered impossible by my reflecting upon it.

This kind of illustration is a characteristic example of where we are led when we try to take account of the fundamental theses of the new quantum mechanics. In all such popularized versions, the absolute object is distinguished from the observing subject after the fashion of the classical theory of knowledge, and the uncertainty relation is traced back to an effect produced by the observer in the absolute object which is different from himself. Thus the impression is given that the impossibility of precise prediction arises simply from the observer's interference with the observed event, and that no conclusion may be drawn as to the non-causal character of the event itself. If we want to go rather more deeply into the secret of the uncertainty relation, we must not rest content with the hypothesis that it arises entirely out of the disturbance caused in the object by the observer. In his contribution to the discussion of causality in *Studium Generale,* von Weizsäcker corrects this misleading explanation of the uncertainty principle, and what he says is worth quoting. 'The popular expositions of quantum mechanics which we physicists have provided have unfortunately contributed to this error. As Niels Bohr has always insisted, the point is not that the act of observing interferes with a situation in the atom as it is in itself, but rather that the physical interaction of observer and object is generally and from the outset a necessary condition of knowledge. From this general principle, which obtains also in classical physics, the quantum-mechanical uncertainty follows because of the additional circumstance which appears in the "dualism experiments", and which can be formulated as follows: The kind of interaction between observer and object which is necessary if certain properties of the object (e.g. its position) are to be displayed, cannot take place simultaneously with the interaction which is necessary if certain other properties (e.g. its momentum) are to be displayed. A disturbance only arises when there is a transition from one kind of interaction to the other. But the choice of a particular kind of interaction, whether it be to initiate it or to maintain it, at once rules out the choice of the "complementary" kind, and therefore leads to the quantum-mechanical uncertainty of such magnitudes as can only be determined by the kind of interaction which has been ruled out. The central point of quantum mechanics is therefore the refusal to describe atomic objects as structures in themselves to which properties such as appear in acts of observation can be ascribed independently of the act of observation itself. Following Bohr, we call this the "denial of objectifiability in atomic events".'

Von Weizsäcker's authentic explanation of the uncertainty-relation helps us to see that this principle, which has dealt the gravest blow to the faith in the inviolability of causal mechanism which was characteristic of classical physics, cannot be made intelligible in the direct intuitive form of the older physics, and certainly not by means of the intuitive notion of an interference in the event arising from a subject who looks at it. We can approach the understanding of this important law only if we accept the radical change in the relation of the self and the world which has come about under the influence of modern physics. This change in the relation of subject and object is embraced within the principle of complementarity which physics first became aware of when the investigation of light yielded the double picture of corpuscle and wave. This dual aspect could only be understood provided that, in distinction from classical physics, the subject and his measuring instruments were from the start included within the picture of the object. According to the choice of experimental procedure, two aspects of the same reality therefore may arise which cannot be held together in one intuition. The same Either/Or holds between them, as Jordan showed, as is found in the psychological field between the state of waking consciousness and the repressions which it forces down into the Unconscious.

The inseparable connection of subject with object which arises within the new view of reality is demonstrated by the fact that instead of thinking in terms of self and world in direct confrontation, we have to work with a variable 'section' which may be placed at different points according to the experiment chosen and the position adopted by the observing subject within the experiment. As laymen we can see something of what is involved by reading the exposition offered by Grete Henry-Hermann who discusses different positions for the 'section' in her essay *Die Kausalität in der Physik (Causality in Physics)* in *Studium Generale Heft 6*, p. 376: 'If, in the process of measurement, the atomic structure which is under investigation has to be illuminated and observed through an optical instrument, then the light which falls from it on to the instrument can either be regarded as a mere means of measurement and thus be taken as part of the instrument, or else its interaction with the atomic object can be pursued in the quantum-mechanical formalism so that it is taken as part of the event which is being investigated. In the former case, the section lies at the point where the light falls upon the atomic structure; in the latter case, it lies at the point where the reflected light meets the instrument.'

We can now look more closely at the fundamental quantum-mechanical equation by which Heisenberg summed up the experimental data of microphysics in 1927 and which is known as the uncertainty-relation. On the basis of Planck's discovery, we understand that there can be no 'actions' in atomic physics which are smaller than Planck's h. These actions are products of momentum and distance, or better of energy and time (erg seconds). It follows therefore that if we wish to determine the place and the momentum (mass × velocity) of an electron or a proton experimentally at the same time, there will be errors in the determination of both magnitudes, but the product of the errors can never be smaller than h. For h can never be sub-divided, and must enter into the calculation only in integral multiples. Thus the more exact the determination of one of these two magnitudes, the less exact will be the other. If the error in one factor, say the space co-ordinate, were reduced to zero, so that the position was exactly determined, the error in the determination of the momentum would be infinitely large. Thus in atomic physics it is impossible to determine exactly and simultaneously both the position and the momentum of a corpuscle.

Determinism and indeterminism are therefore bound up with one another in a unique way in the infinitesimal pro-

cesses out of which reality is composed, if one adopts the standpoint of the new quantum mechanics and its theory of the
processes within the atom.   There is determination of some
kind in view of the fact that the energy contained in this
infinitesimal system remains constant.   When Niels Bohr
postulated 'quantum-jumps' within the atom, using Planck's
quantum theory as his basis, he thought at first that this meant
a breach in the law of the conservation of energy which had
hitherto been absolutely fundamental.   This soon proved to
be a mistake however.   It was shown that the quantum-jumps
of which the electron is capable only alter the form of the
energy, and that the amount remains unaltered.   In any case,
the uncertainty-relation permits of so-called virtual energy
variations, which are complementary to time, and therefore
of very short duration.   Nuclear physics uses these in the
'tunnel effect',[1] and in the theory of nuclear radiations.
(Cf. Flügge: *Einführung in die Kernphysik*, p. 60).   The
energy quantum under consideration, as it appears at time t_2,
is determined from the situation at time t_1 by the principle of
the conservation of energy only up to $h(t_2 - t_1)$.   The full
implications of quantum mechanics would therefore seem to
be that the sum total of the quanta which come to effect in
past, present and future events is constant.   (Dirac's theory
affirms this for light-quanta; cf. the thorough-going exposition
of it from this point of view given by von Neumann, *Mathe-
matische Grundlagen der Quantentheorie*, p. 145.   Born
promises an equally complete theory for material fundamental
particles, but he has not yet produced it.)   At the present
moment, past and future quanta are merely preserved in other
forms of energy.   The history of the world is therefore the
incarnation and revelation of a constant total of units which
is potentially given.   In this constancy of the sum of the
quanta, there is a strong element of determination.   But
against this, the jumps of electrons from one track to another,
and the consequent release of photons, are not determined.
On the contrary, indeed, it must now be said that *the new
quantum mechanics rules out mathematically a deterministic*

---

[1] This concerns passage through a potential barrier, which would be for-
bidden in classical mechanics.

sub-structure. Here, therefore, there remains room for happenings of the kind which have been called a-causal decisions.

14. THE NECESSITY OF NATURAL LAWS AS EXPLAINED BY THE THEORY OF PROBABILITY

Before we introduce the notion of the ' a-causal ', the propriety of which is hotly disputed both from the philosophical and from the scientific standpoints, there remains to be investigated one line of attack on faith in the absolute determination of the course of events in the world. At the same time as the causal-mechanical picture of the world was being upset, an attack was launched from a different direction on the foundations of the whole traditional presentation of causality. The suggestion was that every instance of causal necessity should be interpreted in terms of statistical regularity, and therefore with reference to the average effect of the elementary particles involved in any motion. It was in October 1921 that Walter Nernst first introduced this new interpretation, in his Rectoral Address in Berlin. If even today we refer back to Nernst's Address, that is not because we feel able to take over the thoughts which it contained without modification. This address, after all, was delivered before the foundations were laid of quantum mechanics, something which was not done until 1927-28. A determinate structure was exposed by the principles of quantum mechanics, even in the field of the elementary particles, within the framework of which the indeterminate ' decisions' must remain, even though no deeper basis appeared by which the indeterminate decisions could be rendered intelligible as mass-effects. In this respect therefore many of the presentations of the situation which hold firmly to the Nernst thesis that all natural laws state probabilities only are somewhat out of date.

In the opinion of the critics, the statement that order will come out of universal disorder in accordance with the law of large numbers depends on the condition that the creation is an ' homoömeric' graded hierarchy, at every level of which there are very many self-contained systems of the same or similar order of magnitude. From the outset, therefore, there is already a very far-reaching order which serves as the framework for events conditioned only statistically. The law of large numbers remains therefore a quite substantial problem.

Nernst began the argument of his Rectoral Address from the point that in natural events the most probable state of affairs is always the one which establishes itself. For instance, the molecules of two different gases mix with one another because complete penetration and inter-mixture expresses the condition which has maximum probability. It is perfectly conceivable that two gases should mix with one another for a time, and then separate again. One kind of molecule might collect in the upper half of the container, and the other kind in the lower half. But this does not happen. Something else happens every time, and it is the most probable outcome. Let us take an example which is even clearer than that of the mixture of gases. Suppose that a certain quantity of white sand is put into a vessel, and that an equal quantity of black sand is added to it, the grains of sand being precisely similar apart from their colour. Let us suppose that these piles of different-coloured sand are in the first instance in different parts of the vessel. Then the vessel is thoroughly shaken. The shaking enables the grains of sand to alter their position. But in this movement they do not move according to any calculable pattern. Any motion is equally possible to any one of them. It is quite conceivable that on some occasion the white grains would all collect in the upper part of the vessel and the black grains all be found in the lower part. Or again, the black and white grains may conceivably fall into any given pattern within the vessel, being distributed in definite proportions. But we all know that nothing of this kind ever happens. The more the container is shaken, the clearer it becomes that the tendency is towards a uniform grey mixture which remains the same however long the shaking continues, with slight fluctuations which are extremely important and which provide the subject matter for a special branch of physics. This is the law of large numbers, exhibited in an example. It is a law upon which we rely in regions beyond the sphere of natural science, for instance in popular statistics.

Take the case of the budget presented at the Monte Carlo

Casino at the beginning of the year, when the profits to be expected in the course of the year are calculated with fair accuracy; or the case of the manager of an insurance company who can calculate statistically the number of road accidents to be expected annually; or the statistics which predict the number of suicides or the number of divorces which will take place annually in a large city. Yet it remains true that no insurance company can tell a single one of its clients the probable date of his death. Nevertheless, the company is able to apply a rule for the average number of deaths among its large clientele, and to do it with such accuracy that the business of insurance can be firmly founded thereon. The law of large numbers which is so familiar in the field of vital statistics has its applications also in the field of natural science. We know, for instance, that radio-activity takes place according to a definite law. We know that in the course of about two thousand years half of any given amount of radio-active matter will be exhausted, and that after a further two thousand years half the residue will be exhausted, and so on. And there are other chemical reactions which show the same kind of proportion during specified time intervals. The rule is like that with which the manager of an insurance company works. And the physicist does not know whether a single radium particle which he considers will collapse in the next second, or whether it will remain stable for millions of years to come. He only knows what percentage of the whole amount will be exhausted on the average after two thousand years.

This law of large numbers holds over all the fields of nature where we have to do with masses of infinitesimal particles, and we can take as a particular instance the case of atmospheric pressure which is accounted for by the impact of air molecules. The atmospheric pressure on a box is the same on the top as on the bottom, since the effect of the impact of the air molecules is the same on both sides, but this is because the average effect of a huge number of air molecules comes to the same thing in the case of either side. The number of molecules involved goes in quadrillions. The probability of a slight difference in what is happening on either side, even one which persists only for a very short time, is so remote in view of the huge number of molecules, that it is of no practical consequence. On the other hand, if we make the surface which is exposed to atmospheric pressure very much smaller, and in fact reduce it to a square whose side measures 0·001 mm., the difference in pressure will eventually become so noticeable that we can observe a small displacement of the surface in a microscope. This is the Brownian movement, which may also be observed microscopically in the case of the tiny particles of fat in diluted milk.

If we are confronted with the law of large numbers in the case of atoms and molecules, for instance air molecules, this is even more likely to happen in the case of the electrons with which we have to do in atomic physics.

Let us take an example from the behaviour of electrons which can readily be envisaged. A beam of electrons, travelling in the same direction with the same velocity but moving independently of each other and with no inherent mutual order, falls obliquely upon a very thin crystal surface. A certain percentage which can be precisely determined will be reflected from the crystal, and the rest will pass through it. But if a single electron with this same velocity falls upon the surface at the same angle, it will either be reflected, or it will pass through. For the electron is a whole, and so far it is impossible to think of it being divided into two parts. The law of the reflection of electrons from a crystal is therefore a statistical law. It serves only to determine the behaviour of a large number of electrons, and says nothing whatever about the behaviour of a single electron. What is divided, when a single electron meets the crystal surface is not the electron itself, but the probability that the electron will do one of two possible things. Here, therefore, we have an indeterminate event.

This brings us to the point where the interpretation of causality in natural laws in terms of probability theory agrees with the quantum-mechanical disruption of faith in the absolute determination of events. When the number of elementary events or of ultimate elements out of which reality is built becomes large enough, they come under the law of large numbers. These elementary events are Planck's *h*-

quanta. And these have an infinitesimally small value. As a rule, therefore, we are not dealing with thousands of them, but with trillions or quadrillions. With such inconceivable numbers of elementary actions, the law of what happens is exact enough in practice in virtue of the law of large numbers. For the probability of any noticeable deviation is practically nil.

15. THE DISPUTE CONCERNING ULTIMATE CONSEQUENCES FOR OUR WORLD-VIEW

It is evident that faith in the absolute determination of events has been profoundly disrupted, and that this disruption lies behind the dispute in modern physics between determinism and indeterminism. There is complete agreement about the Uncertainty-Principle, which served to shatter the causal-mechanical world-picture, and similarly there is agreement about the importance of statistics for the understanding of many laws of the macrocosmic world. But as soon as the question is raised, on the basis of these conclusions, about the ultimate consequences for our world-view, there is deep division of opinion, and two opposing standpoints are found among the scientists. On the one side there are the physicists who say with Heisenberg that quantum mechanics has demonstrated for all time that a universal rigid causal law has no validity. On the other side there are men like Max Planck, Einstein, von Laue and, on the biological side, Max Hartmann, who raise the objection that no one can say with certainty today that quantum physics in its present state, where the causal law is called into question, represents the last word; that electrons and protons, together with photons, are really to be taken as the ultimate elements of the physical world, and that there can never be more refined elements, or more refined measurements of the current fundamental particles. The progress of physical knowledge is an unending progress. Any judgment which asserts the final validity of a certain structure of natural reality is a mythological and metaphysical opinion which rests on nothing by way of proof. The monistic theory of Laplace, and the probability theory of quantum physics are both metaphysical assumptions, incapable of proof, and they trespass beyond the bounds of natural science (Max Hartmann, *Universitas*, March 1948, p. 322).

Laymen, of course, cannot interfere in this dispute which has broken out among the scientists about the ultimate validity of causality. But one thing we can say. It is certainly conceivable that new avenues will open in the science of the future, and that new discoveries will be made which will require a revision of the conclusions which have been reached in modern atomic physics. Nothing is inherently impossible in the field of progressive science. Hitherto, however, it has been fundamental to human thinking that the advances of natural science should be in the direction of the limitless. But they tend not to be steps backward. After the Copernican discovery was once made, we were not able to return to the point of view of primitive thinkers who believed that the sun moved round the earth inside the vault of heaven. After the discovery of the law of the conservation of energy by Julius Robert Mayer, this law has not been repudiated despite all the transformation in physics. The same thing will be true of Planck's discovery of the *h*-content on which quantum physics is built.

The great question which is at stake in modern physics is whether the revolution which has brought us out of classical physics into quantum-mechanical thinking is in fact a complete revolution, applying to the whole of our picture of nature, or whether it applies only to realities of a given order of magnitude, and whether, therefore, behind the world of electrons, protons and neutrons there may be a still more subtle world, hidden from us, whose fundamental particles behave according to the laws of classical physics. This question clearly cannot be settled today by purely scientific observations. It is a question of principle which can only be settled, if at all, by surveying the world in all its ranges. Contradictions which we cannot resolve will remain as between the scientists. We can only take care that the principal point at issue remains clear, that the opposing parties confront each other squarely, and that the matter is not obscured by mutual misunderstandings. There are two points where there is still a measure of obscurity, and where clarification is called for.

The first of the points which are still obscure is the much disputed notion of the a-causal. It is the common opinion that an event which cannot be explained causally can only be arbitrary. More precisely, it must be an act of freedom, a decision such as is made by a man who has a free will. This leads to the suggestion that an event such as the disintegration of a radium nucleus, which, according to statistical observation, happens once every two thousand years, and happens in a way for which no grounds can be adduced, must be an event something like the decision of a human will; that the radium nucleus which explodes must be a psychic entity which ventures upon a death leap and commits suicide. But when I call an event a-causal, I intend nothing beyond the simple negative which the term expresses. Something happens here for which no ground can be adduced. 'But', it is said, 'it must have some kind of ground.' But this is not in the least necessary, for whenever we attempt to trace back some fact to its ultimate origin, we come sooner or later to the point where we must rest content with what is ultimately ungrounded and inexplicable. For example, we see an avalanche crashing into the valley, and we wish to track this event back to the place where high on the mountain side a lump of snow is displaced and receives the initial impulse which sets the whole motion in train. But when we have traced the incident back to this point, we are confronted with the further question as to why the mass of snow rolled at all. The answer is because the law of gravitation holds good. But why does this law hold good? It may be that we can trace this back to a 'metric field'. All our explanations always come back to some ultimate inexplicable fundamental law. In the end we are left with so-called axioms which we must simply accept as given. In one of his latest writings, P. Jordan says: 'We can regard the axioms only as empirically given.' Here then we stand confronted with the pure notion of the a-causal, without which, despite Kant's category of causality, we can reach no explanations. The a-causal is the presupposition of any explanation. The question cannot be whether this notion is generally admissible, but simply whether we may employ it at places other than the axioms and fundamental data of our existence, for instance in the case of the motion of fundamental particles.

A second point where there is a certain amount of confusion in the dispute about causality in modern physics is the question as to how the statistical interpretation of natural laws is related to the causal principle. M. Hartmann brings forward the following objection against the interpretation of natural laws given by probability theory: 'In a chaotic condition of cosmic reality, a state of affairs where fundamental particles behaved in a free and arbitrary manner, no order and no regularity would be possible at all, not even those of a statistical or probability kind' (M. Hartmann, *Atomphysik, Biologie und Religion,* p. 17; cf. also *Universitas,* March 1948, p. 322). He remarks, as against Jordan: 'Instead of being content with the plain statement that we know only the statistical rules for the disintegration in time of radium atoms, and that the basis on which such rules rest is completely unknown (there must be some ground for them, since in a chaos both lawlessness and statistical regularity would be alike indemonstrable), P. Jordan suggests that we feel tempted to say that the single radium atom decides for itself when it will disintegrate. All that can be generally established is a regular tendency of the radium atoms to disintegrate, and this shows itself in the statistical law of their disintegration. Within the room for manœuvre which is thus available, the single atom has extensive freedom to decide on its own disintegration' (Hartmann, *Universitas,* March 1948, p. 328).

If we have understood these sentences aright, Hartmann is reckoning with three possibilities. The first is that the course of nature always and everywhere has the character which we have hitherto grasped in the macroscopic realm in terms of classical physics. The second is that the course of nature proceeds according to the statistical rules of probability, so that the causal law no longer holds exactly but has gaps. The third possibility is pure chaos, so-called, or the chaotic condition of complete irregularity, with free arbitrary behaviour of the fundamental particles.   In this case 'no order or regularity is possible at all, not even those of a statistical or probability kind'.

These remarks show that, in this discussion between the scientists, what is at issue is not just a difference of biological or physical opinion, but a difference on a much deeper level. The standpoint to which we have moved, particularly since W. Nernst took us beyond the old understanding of natural laws, and from which du Nouy for example as a biologist has framed the fundamental theses of his work on the essence of life, may be described like this.   The third of Hartmann's possibilities, where there is no order, not even of a statistical probability kind, is certainly not the case.   Chaos, complete irregularity, obtains (and then only in appearance) where we have to do with small numbers.   As soon as we are dealing with millions and myriads, the probability coefficient, the law of large numbers, at once becomes apparent.   For any manifold of data of the homoömeric kind, whatever its character be—the most wild intermingling or a chaos in which everything is continually being stirred up together, is already, from the point of view of the law of probability, an initial condition within that region for the law of large numbers to hold, and from this initial condition the law will operate to give definite results which are the more exact the greater the number of entities involved.   The condition in which a mass of entities is uniformly mixed according to a given rule—the example used by W. Nernst of a mixture of black-and-white sand is a case in point—is not of such a kind that no order obtains there, despite the fact that in themselves the black and white grains of sand take up any and every conceivable relation to one another.   The longer the mixture is shaken up, and the greater the quantity of sand involved, the closer we approximate to the condition where numbers which are virtually constant emerge.   For those who represent the probability-theory point of view about natural laws, it is therefore not the case, as Hartmann seems to suggest, that this explanation may be offered tentatively in respect of the microcosmic world where we have to do with other orders of magnitude, whereas in a higher order the old laws of nature still hold. Rather is it the case, as maintained by Nernst and also by de Nouy, that if the law of large numbers only holds in the region of the infinitesimals, we must nevertheless extend this interpretation to the whole of nature, and must apply it equally to the largest as well as to the smallest objects.

16. CONSEQUENCES FOR THE BELIEF IN GOD

Let us now once more look back, in order to draw out ultimate implications for our world-view from what has been said in preceding sections. We started from the fact that every event in time leads into the future with a degree of uncertainty. Here we recall the example of the steam hammer at the Krupp works. Only what has already happened is certain and able to stand before us objectively. Anything which belongs to the future contains always an uncertain component which may be great or small. We feel that we could move happily into the future and handle it with complete security if this uncertain component which haunts all our plans could be reduced to zero. We see practical evidence of this in the careful steps taken within the scientific movement by practical concentration of the will to remove all uncertainty, in the hope that a desired result may thus be obtained with the greatest possible assurance. Something very similar happens in the case of Indian fakirs when they produce miracles by this means. So far, however, we have not been concerned with the questions of miracles, but rather with causality. We have taken the various accounts of causal happening as different means by which to limit as far as possible the uncertainty component which invests with insecurity all our human conduct. We saw that essentially there are three ways by which this has been done.

The first way is the faith of Laplace in a course of nature which is calculable in every detail, the laws of which we only need to know in order to conduct our technical affairs in accordance with it.

The second way is the empirico-positivist thesis that everything proceeds by the law of chance, but that we are entitled to believe that an event which has taken place regularly hitherto (as, for instance, the daily rising of the sun) is to be expected in the future the more confidently the greater be the number of times it has already happened, so that we can commit ourselves to the future with an expectation of the event in question, on the ground of its repetition in the past.

The third way is the Kantian enterprise of working out *a priori* the process of things to come, by a critique of human reason.

When all these three ways have been shown to be untenable, nothing remains save the purely negative escape, which in reality is not an escape at all, but an assertion that for us men there is no escape from the impenetrability of the future. It is the view expounded in Heidegger's *Sein und Zeit*, that the road into the future is a road into the night, a road which we must however traverse, because, by reason of our existence in time, we are 'held within the Void'.

The question now is whether, beside these four ways, there is still a fifth possibility, or whether all our human possibilities have been exhausted by them? Such a fifth possibility to become lord of the future is available only if we hold fast to the word spoken by Jesus and treasured by His Church from the beginning, so that anxiety about the future may be overcome. It is necessary to give the different variants of this saying in order to draw from it our further reflections. 'Verily I say unto you, Whosoever shall say unto this mountain, Be thou taken up and cast into the sea; and shall not doubt in his heart, but shall believe that what he saith cometh to pass; he shall have it' (Mark 11.23-4).

The power of this word of Christ comes home to us only when, as in this section, we have first set out all the human efforts to dispel doubt about the future through reasoning or experience. In this first, and earliest, version of Christ's saying He is concerned with the dispelling of doubt. Only when that is so does it enlist a sympathetic hearing. Everything depends on the triumphant dispelling of the last remnant of the uncertainty component of which we spoke. That everything depends on this may be seen from the second version of the saying: 'Verily I say unto you, If ye have faith as a grain of mustard seed, ye shall say unto this mountain, Remove hence to yonder place; and it shall remove, and nothing shall be impossible unto you' (Matt. 17.20).

By way of illustration of this word of the Saviour, we may refer to the story of the healing of the epileptic boy in Mark 9.14-29, with the impressive cry of the sorely tried father: 'Lord, I believe; help thou mine unbelief.' In this cry of a man wrestling with faith, it is made plain that everything depends on the fact that the residue of unbelief, the subjugation of which is at stake here, should completely disappear, so that the way may then be open for victorious faith. But how can it be done? Not through the strenuous efforts of a man, attempting by concentration of will to suppress the uncertainty component. Here we are dealing with something different. We can make clear what it is only by trying to think, not in terms of content but in terms of 'spaces', as we are attempting to do throughout this book. This thinking in terms of spaces and spatial dimensions begins, as we saw in the previous volume, where we make a clear distinction between the space of I and Thou, and the space of bodies with its three spatial and one temporal dimensions. This brings us to two different forms of polar space. Then comes the decisive step, for which everything else serves as preparation, namely the discovery of the supra-polar world-space which is our introduction to the sphere of the supra-mundane and the eternal.

The word of Christ indicates the discovery of the supra-polar space, by which at one blow the last remnant of the uncertainty component disappears, in that it shows a disappearance of uncertainty about future expectation, and therefore of doubts about whether prayer is heard, and about the occurrence of miraculous healings which have been the subject of prayer. Previously, a twilight state of affairs prevailed. On the one hand there was the light of a faint hope that prayer is heard, and on the other the night of doubt and 'unbelief' where this hope was beset with alternative possibilities. Now, upon this twilight there breaks the victorious light of faith's certainty. The whole mystery of the power of miracles is wrapped up in the word 'faith', and of course it is upon miracles that the discussion focuses at this point. What is the meaning of the word 'faith'? Clearly it does not mean any human action such as trust, or the acceptance of invisible realities as true. The term faith has a much more comprehensive significance. This begins to dawn upon us only when we begin to think in terms of 'spaces'. Faith is the mode by which we exist in a space, by which we live from its resources, and are utterly rooted and grounded in it. We know what this means directly in the case of the polar spaces whose entities are directly presented to us, an obvious instance being three-dimensional physical space from which emerges the whole materialistic-mechanical world-picture. If a miracle happens, and supra-polar space is opened to us, then it is possible for us to stand in supra-polar space in just the same way as hitherto we have been standing in three-dimensional physical space. Faith is then the being of the whole man in the supra-polar space. Just as we stand with our entire existence in the physical world, so now we stand in the supra-polar sphere and we become invested with all the powers which here are present all around us. It is when we think this through, with all that it means, that we begin to realize what Jesus meant by the word faith. We grasp why Jesus laid such stress upon faith, and why, according to His words, faith is the key which opens all the doors into the eternal world; the power which overwhelms all the powers of the earth, so that a man who believes is able to 'remove mountains into the sea'. Thus Jesus says to Martha: 'Said I not unto thee, that, if thou believedst, thou shouldest see the glory of God?' (John 11.40); and to the father of the epileptic boy: 'Everything is possible to him who believes.' It is clear in all these phrases what is meant by the word faith is not a human effort, for the smallest and weakest of human beings are summoned to believe without further ado. As was seen in the previous volume, it is particularly clear in the ages of persecution and martyrdom that the power of faith does not reside in heroic personalities, but that the weakest of men participate therein. Faith is not conditioned by any kind of human powers, but simply by the fact that the human will rests in God in complete surrender. This repose in God is the sole postulate for prayer to be heard and answered and for the experience of miraculous powers.

It is in connection with the word faith, to which we have now been led, that we reach the point where the notion of the a-causal, with which physics and biology are so pre-occupied, comes to its own. The course of our enquiries in the previous volume began from the point that something exists which sets the limit for our objective knowledge. This is the riddle of our own personal existence, the primary datum given to us before we set eyes on any object at all. It is the *I* which must always be presupposed before we confront any object. My *I* is not this physical organism which is all that appears to my neighbour, nor is it the world of my conscious-ness, the wealth of visual images, sensations, ideas, memories, dreams, pleasures, pains or motions of the will. All this is merely the wealth of objects which parade in uninterrupted succession before my *I* here and now, as before a spectator. As Fritz Künkel once said, I can speak of my *I* only negatively, by denying of it all the statements which can be made about objective things. Can anything at all be said about it there-fore, or does nothing remain for me except to be silent? One thing must in any case be said. My *I* is granted to me in a way I do not understand. Heidegger says that 'I am thrown into my existence'. That I am at this point, and not at any other where I might equally well have been cast, contains the whole riddle of my destiny. If we ask whence it comes that I have been cast into this place, we can only answer that here we are confronted with the a-causal; for the necessity by which I am here is neither a mechanical necessity, which could be assessed in the Laplace sense, nor is it one which can be explained in terms of Hume's causal theory, nor can it be deduced from any necessity of reason in the Kantian fashion. Here we have to deal with an absolute accident, and therefore, in the last resort, with an inexplicable a-causal datum. Thus therefore we have reached the goal indicated in this present section which has dealt with absolute determination. We affirm something to which we have been led by the last three sections. In each of these sections we traced the collapse of an absolute in which men had sought an anchorage for thought and life. This collapse, which was not a merely speculative matter but was the result of experimental work, serves in every case to make room for the true Absolute.

The first absolute, built by man for himself, was the absolute object which materialism served to absolutize. This first material absolute collapsed when it appeared that subject and object are inextricably bound up together, so that it is impossible to separate the object from the *I* and to absolutize it thus.

The second absolute in which men sought refuge was absolute space and absolute time, as Newton believed in them. But every point of orientation which it was hoped to establish in this absolute space was relativized on further reflection, and all the anchorages which men sought were lost hopes. In the end, there was nothing save the alpha-body, a fiction postulated by man, to which even so he was not able to anchor himself.

The last absolute which we have considered, and the one of greatest practical significance, was causal necessity, the hand-rail to which men clung when the future loomed over them like a dark storm cloud. As we have seen, this is faith in a causal necessity which may be conceived under the most diverse forms, that of mechanical predictability, or that of necessities of reason, or that of faith in the repetition of what has often happened before. It is characteristic of our age, however, that this faith in causal necessity, and all the consequences which have been deduced from it, have suffered a blow which has brought it to the point of collapse as never before. This collapse is not the result of doubt about mechanical laws or about *a priori* conditions of knowledge. Its ground lies much deeper in the essence of our whole existence, namely in the temporality of that existence. This rules out all certainty about the future, and plunges us into the Void which looms over us. But the collapse which confronts us here serves only to clear the way for a sight of God. It is a collapse which relates only to the polar mode of being in which we are imprisoned. This alone is built on the fundamental principle that only what belongs to the past is certain, and that everything future is accompanied, as we explained above, by an uncertainty component. This fundamental principle is the impassable frontier within which our whole polar existence is once for all enclosed and beyond which we cannot force our way. But from this negative thesis there follows a very important positive one. We cannot reach this further step in our own power. If it is possible at all for us to go beyond this frontier the possibility is one which can only be granted to us. It is not an internal frontier, like those which mark off one country from another. It does not enclose a certain region within which certain laws hold. It is rather a 'spatial' frontier which marks off an existence where a given thing is impossible from another realm of being where that particular possibility is real. Jesus points to this difference in being when He said to Martha: 'If thou believedst, thou shouldest see the glory of God.' By belief Jesus meant an existence within a new space which is inaccessible from polar space in either of its forms. Access to this supra-polar space of God's omnipresence is something which has to be directly granted to us by God. If that happens, we have above all else a new vision of the significance of our own *I*. It is peculiarly important for our own time, when everything around us seems to be involved in unending upheaval and continuous change, that we should recognize in the light of faith that amidst the ceaseless motion the *I*, the greatest gift we have received from God, is something eternal which remains the same through all the changes of the visible world.

So far, however, we have produced nothing more than a few preliminary observations which serve to clarify the all-important fundamental notion which is the subject of dispute in current argument about the problem of causality. Now at last we propose to think the matter through to its end.

All the chapters which have been written thus far bring us back, each in its own way, to the ancient command of God, and set it in a new light: 'I am the Lord, thy God, thou shalt have no other gods beside me.' In political history, in the history of thought, and finally in natural science, a new absolute is constantly being set upon the throne which belongs to God alone. Man goes on absolutizing one worldly magnitude after another in order to erect upon it his world-structure. And each time we see a new variation on the same process by which the absolute raised against God by men is destroyed. The destruction is not achieved by the apologetic methods practised by priests and philosophers in defence of their dogmas. The altars built by men as their places of devotion are demolished from within by the process of discovery which goes forward irresistibly to embrace new aspects of reality. Thus the absolute object in which all materialisms put their trust collapsed when atomic physics penetrated into the infinitesimal world. Newton's absolute space and absolute time, in which men sought refuge and anchorage in face of the boundless deeps of universal reality, collapsed by reason of new discoveries made by the human mind in the course of its investigations into the dimensions of space and time.

And now, in the last chapter, we reached the most important absolute, one to which men have always been driven back in the practical conduct of life; namely the causal determination of the world process. This faith in the causal-mechanical world-picture is the anchorage which a man supposes himself most urgently to need because he is required at each moment of his daily life to leave the firm ground of what is given and already decided and commit himself blindly to the waves of the as yet undecided future. One may compare him with a courageous steersman who must risk his ship among the tossing waves on a stormy night. He requires not only a chart to give him his orientation in respect of what awaits him and prevent his coming to grief on the invisible rocks which threaten him on either side, but he also needs faith in the causal necessity of events in the world process, as those events condition one another, so that he can deduce with a certain measure of security what is yet to come from what has already happened. The faith expressed most clearly by the mathematician Laplace gives man this world-picture and the requisite faith in firm causal connections by which all experiences of the objective world, including those in the future, are bound together. The distinctive feature of this faith of Laplace was not the possibility of deducing all events, forwards and backwards, with mathematical certainty. Obviously such calculations can and must include errors if they were to be attempted in practice. The distinctive thing which gave to the causal-mechanical world-view its peculiar power and made it serve as a firm basis for the blossoming technics of the modern age was the assurance that these errors in calculation could not have their roots in objective reality. Their roots could only lie in a subjective source of error, namely in human short-sightedness, blindness and uncertainty about the state of the world. All the mistakes which cropped up in their calculations, even those with calamitous consequences, could not therefore ever upset the men of the technical epoch, for this faith which characterized the causal-mechanical age was always nothing more than the belief that the whole world process was in principle susceptible of absolute and infallible calculation. This faith in the absolute validity of the causal law within objective reality is manifestly the fourth absolute upon which the technical age was founded. And once men had put their whole trust in it, it could never be shattered, even though it meant reckoning with grave catastrophes like the collapse of the Tay Bridge.

It is only a man who has lived with this firm faith in the objective infallibility of the causal-mechanical world-picture, and who has made his technical developments on the basis of it, who is in a position to know the earth-shaking quality of the disturbance which has run through the very foundations of modern technics, when a leading physicist like Heisenberg is prepared to say that, by reason of the discoveries of modern atomic physics, the causal law which was valid in the age of causal mechanism has now lost its validity. It is not the case that everything must be viewed as necessary, for a great many things may only be understood with reference to the law of probability. Here what is involved is not merely some particular calamity, however severe, which threatens the technical realm, but rather the objective constitution of reality itself as it is laid open to the scientists who press deep into the innermost heart of this reality with their experiments and calculations.[1]

If it is true that there has been a disruption of the innermost foundations upon which faith in the universal validity of the causal law as hitherto understood rested, the question to be faced is this: How is man to deal with this new situation where the entire picture of reality which has obtained hitherto is suddenly altered? Two possibilities are available. The first attitude which seems to be possible in face of the new situation is the one advocated by Martin Heidegger in his book, *Sein und Zeit,* as exhibiting the true significance of being. It is precisely the man of our own time, contemplating the ruins of the old causal-mechanical faith, who discovers in his time the exposition of existence which Heidegger provides, and finds it to be an interpretation of his own innermost existence which, as such, appeals to him in a quite special degree. The existentialism of Jean Paul Sartre is very much under the influence of Heidegger, though Heidegger himself regards this existentialism as a misunderstanding of his own philosophy. But if, with Heidegger, we include being in time as among the essentials of human existence, so that the *I* who exists does not merely 'stand out' (*existere*) in the past and the present but also into the uncertain future, then it belongs to the essence of our being that we are thrown or pitchforked into death, the death which determines our life at each moment thereof. We are 'held within the Void', and therefore, apart from any question of temperament, we are involved in *Angst* (dread) and *Sorge* (anxiety) in face of a reality which is steadily coming upon us in threatening fashion. This attitude, of which Heidegger has given the most impressive description, arises when faith has been lost in the inner anchorage which is afforded, for instance, by certainty about the future, calculation of what the future entails, and conviction about the eternal validity of natural laws. There is, however, a second possibility open to men.

[1] The principles of the conservation of energy and impulse must still be maintained with the character of a causal nexus. Nuclear physics relies upon their application to particular elementary processes (the trigger effect), and its success goes to confirm the application. The uncertainty-principle gives rise to particular variations in this field.

We begin to understand its content when we see that there is available an inner support which is described in the New Testament in the words of Jesus not as some kind of theoretical conviction but as new existence, something which is diametrically opposed to Heidegger's *Grundbefindlichkeit* (basic attitude) and which alone is competent to deliver us from it. That which Heidegger describes as dread or anxiety in face of an unknown which is coming upon us, or as our 'being held within the Void', is challenged by the powerful word of Jesus: 'Be not afraid! Are not two sparrows sold for a farthing? And not one of them shall fall on the ground without your Father. But the very hairs of your head are all numbered. Fear not, therefore; ye are of more value than many sparrows' (Matt. 10.29ff.). 'Be not therefore anxious for the morrow, for the morrow will be anxious for itself. Sufficient unto the day is the evil thereof' (Matt. 6.34). It strikes us immediately how radically these well-known sayings of Jesus contradict the description of human *Grundbefindlichkeit* which, according to Heidegger, emerges directly from our being in time. The new existence which here appears as the other possibility for man, and which alone is competent to overcome the mode of being which is the result of our temporality and to take it off its hinges, clearly rests on the fact that we are not 'held within the Void', but rather within a new supra-polar space pertaining to the presence of a higher all-powerful 'I' who knows about us and our destiny and who is concerned about everything which may cause us anxiety. The supra-polarity of this higher *I* appears from the fact that it stands outside the whole polar relationship in which relative *I*-beings like ourselves stand to one another, and in virtue of which we are continually bounded and restricted. Only a supra-polar *I*, which is beyond all these restrictions, has unlimited powers of disposal over all things. Jesus says of the Father: 'With God all things are possible.' And now all the anxiety without which it is impossible for us to exist as we advance without assurance or defence into an entirely unknown future collapses immediately if what Jesus says about God is true: 'Not a sparrow falls to the ground without your Father. The very hairs of your head are all numbered.' In the light of our present knowledge of nature, these words are of outstanding significance. If Jesus wished to put the point of God's complete sovereignty, we might have expected that He would use entirely different illustrations. We might well have supposed that Jesus would refer to the great events in world history where world empires, arising from the ocean of history, collapse back in impotence to make room for other world powers; or that He would refer to world catastrophes, where, perhaps through a single discovery or invention, the face of the earth has suddenly been transformed; and that He would point out how the Almighty stands behind these far-reaching revolutionary episodes, and guides them with His mighty hand. Such instances of God's omnipotence would seem to us to be the most impressive. Instead of this, Jesus points to the smallest and most trivial things that happen on earth as illustrations of the Father's power, as when a bird from one casual flock falls dead to the ground without anyone noticing it, or when a man loses a hair. Today, in the era of atomic research, we might say: No quantum-jump happens without your Father in heaven. The saying shines in its true light in the context of current atomic physics. Here we are facing a fundamental law which runs through the whole of creation. All events, however great, we now know to be the cumulation of decisions which occur in the infinitesimal realm.

To clarify matters further let us again look at the example taken from the animal world, the nuptial dance of the may-fly which can be seen on summer evenings on any river bank. From a distance this remarkable spectacle appears like a cloud or some kind of smoke formation pulsating with a mysterious form of life. When it is studied more closely it is a formal dance carried out by thousands of tiny beings. Each of these beings pursues its own individual course and makes, as it would seem, its own decisions; nevertheless all these single individuals are simply members of a whole whose object is to fulfil the command of fruitfulness and the continuation of the species. As soon as this aim is achieved, the individuals drop back into the dark stream which carries their corpses away.

Or we might use an illustration drawn from the behaviour of traffic. Think of an airman flying over a large city at such a height that the stream of traffic thronging in the narrow streets appears as a black serpentine line which moves on uniformly, halting only at certain crossings as though at a given sign, and moving on again after a given time. From the height which the airman has attained it is impossible to see that this black serpentine structure is composed of individual men each of whom acts in accordance with his own decisions. Here is a parallel to the mysterious mass movement which the fundamental particles carry out in accordance with the law of large numbers. The average motion which is achieved in this way will attain to a greater degree of uniformity the larger be the number of elementary parts from which the average effect is produced. Men like ourselves who can observe only macroscopically, so that the sub-atomic world is concealed from us, resemble the airman who is flying at such a height that he is able to perceive only the total average effect, which is all that we can perceive in respect of any body in our neighbourhood. The reality with which we have to do is always therefore such a mass formation which composes itself into a determinate framework through the cumulation of many single events.

The great belief on which, according to the saying of Jesus in the Sermon on the Mount, everything turns, and which alone is able to give us peace and freedom from anxiety in the midst of storm-ridden world processes, is the belief that precisely in this region of the small and simple it is not an impersonal causal mechanism which rules, but a personal will which guides every elementary particle, without which no sparrow falls to the ground and no hair can fall from our heads. 'Without the Father,' says Jesus, not one of these smallest events takes place, and the world process is constituted by their interplay. This does not mean that it is the Father who kills the sparrow or extracts the hair. Jesus says only that each of the smallest events within the created world does not take place without the Father. Each is taken up into the all-embracing space of the presence of the Almighty. No creature dies alone, not even one of the innumerable birds of the air. Each one, dying, falls back into the bosom of the Father from which it proceeded, and realizes the nearness of the Father even in its death.

From the time when these words were uttered in this world, humanity has been required to decide as between two representations of the world. The first of these world aspects is the causal mechanical one with all its possible variations, which Laplace brought to the supreme point of expression. On this view, which is still shared by the majority of men today, it is an impersonal and indefinable necessity which initiates and maintains the motion in all events, great and small. It is not of supreme importance whether this necessity be carried back to a mechanical law or to an inexplicable accident. The decisive point is always what kind of subject stands behind the whole happening; what kind of original power holds the universe on its course. According to this first and generally widespread view, the moving force is a blind impersonal soulless power. To its sovereignty we can only submit fatalistically like a caravan submerged by a sandstorm in the desert. The camels lay their heads in the sand and let everything pass over them. Alternatively we might observe its effects and do our calculations and build our mechanical contrivances on the basis of these calculations. It is impossible to come into any kind of personal contact with the power that moves all things. It remains eternally foreign to us, remote and incomprehensible. The scientist Gustav Theodor Fechner called a representation of the world which is based on this theory the 'night view'. For the indefinable power which keeps all things in motion is in any case unconscious. Conscious beings like ourselves cannot come into union with it. On all sides, therefore, we are surrounded by the deep night of an unconscious world. *I*-beings such as we are resemble solitary lights in the midst of this profound night which is all around us; lights which illuminate the great darkness at some points and create small areas of radiance, but only for a short time during which they themselves are alight, after which the deep night in which they shine swallows them up as well. What Fechner is saying here is what Heidegger means when he says that we are held within the Void with the great darkness of death bearing down upon us. To this 'night view', to which men subscribe whether they are aware of it or not, Jesus opposes the 'day view' when He speaks about the victory over fear; the view which consists in the faith that nothing, not even the motions of the infinitesimal particles, happens without the Father, who wills everything and knows everything and with whom conscious beings may stand in uninterrupted personal relationship. As soon as this great faith, in which Jesus lived continually, has been granted to us, it is as though we had been delivered out of complete night and morning had dawned within us which itself is the prelude of day. However deep the suffering in which we happen to be involved, it is bright day all around us; for the omnipresence of the supra-polar Spirit of God is round us, and everything is bathed in the light of eternity. An eternal Thou accompanies every step of our lives. We are able to talk to Him about everything, and He alone attends to our every word, even when our fellow men have left us to pine away in a dark dungeon. This day view of the world which Jesus lived out in His relation with the Father is not one that can be established on philosophical grounds, nor through scientific observations of any kind whatever. With all our ideas and proofs we are not able to take one step beyond the polar world. All scientific observations and calculations are implacably subordinated to the law of polarity. As we maintained in the first volume of this book, there is only one way by which to experience the reality of the supra-polar realm which, according to Psalm 139, surrounds us on every side. Luther says: *via in coelum est linea indivisibilis puncti nempe conscientiae*, which means that the way to heaven is a line which passes through an indivisible point, namely conscience. No kind of intellectual proof or ground of understanding or set of conclusions drawn from this world where we live can lead us to this goal. We reach it only when a command, and with it an unavoidable task, enters into our conscience, and at one stroke makes real to us a reality other than this world, so that it is impossible for us to evade it. When Paul received the task which gave direction to his whole life to the moment of his death, he said: 'A necessity is laid upon me. Woe to me if

I do not preach the Gospel. For if I am doing this of my own will I have a reward; but if not of my own will I am entrusted with a commission' (I Cor. 9.16-17). Luther's experience was the same, when he said before the Diet of Worms: 'My conscience is bound to God's Word, and to act against the conscience is unsafe and perilous.' It is by this road which leads through conscience, and not by way of intellectual grounds nor by way of the motions of sentiment, that the certainty of a supra-polar space is granted to us, in which God is omnipresent around us. From this point alone do we lay hold on the words of Jesus about the omnipotence of the omnipresent God which holds even in the smallest details of reality. As we realize at once, it does not immediately follow that the course of nature is interrupted by miracles. The point is simply that behind what happens, whether it be entirely natural or miraculous, there stands at every moment the living God who makes Himself known to us in conscience. One of the most significant points about the Scriptures in accordance with which Christ lived is that the word 'causality' never occurs in them, nor does the word 'fate' or 'destiny'. All these unpersonal expressions, which are constantly in use in philosophy, and also in science, are entirely absent from the Bible, and in place of them there is always the one all-sovereign personality of the living God who guides all things. God's omnipresence is the space filling everything, into which the relative spaces of this world are fitted. No conflict can therefore arise between the rule of God and any natural laws which we are able to establish by observation. For biblical man everything is reduced to the fact that behind all events and behind all the orders of the world there stands the living God as the directing power. According to Scripture, God is a God of order. Therefore any order which obtains in this world is a disposition or ordinance from God. After the cosmic catastrophe of the Flood, God re-establishes the order of nature as a gift of grace to the human beings who have been saved through the catastrophe. 'While the earth remaineth, seed-time and harvest, cold and heat, summer and winter, day and night shall not cease' (Gen. 8.22). The passage about the order of nature in Jeremiah is of even greater significance: 'If my covenant of day and night stand not, if I have not appointed the ordinances of heaven and earth, then will I also cast away the seed of Jacob, and of David my servant' (Jer. 33.25). The ordinances of the world are therefore not natural necessities which can be explained simply from a causal nexus. Rather are they personal ordinances of the omnipotent will, the product of God's covenant with the forces of nature, which covenant can be compared with the covenant God enters into with the people whom He has selected for a particular purpose out of all the nations.

In the Bible, therefore, we are dealing from the outset with a thoroughly personal view of nature, where everything that happens in this world is seen in the light of the personal government of the world. When a tornado wrecks the tents of Job, or when his servants and his cattle are destroyed in the course of an attack by robber bands, Job can say with deep conviction: 'The Lord gave, and the Lord hath taken away. Blessed be the name of the Lord.' When David, having been heavily defeated, is cursed and stoned by Shimei (II Sam. 16), the reason being a thirst for vengeance arising from the feud between Saul's family and David, David forbids his men to take action, saying: 'Let him alone and let him curse, for the Lord hath bidden him.' The conviction that God's world is under the sway of demonic powers which have rebelled against Him, and that at the end there will appear a great opponent of God, belongs, as we shall see later, to this personal view of history and of nature. Why such a conviction was necessary can best be indicated in a later context. Here we must be content with the preliminary observation that the conflict which arises in virtue of the inexplicable rebellion of Satan is of a purely personal character, and it is from this standpoint alone that it can be understood.

From all this it appears that the final absolute which plays its part in philosophy and science, namely the absolute determination of events through an iron law of causality which may assume many forms, is from the biblical point of view an idol erected by the human mind in opposition to the sole sovereignty of the living God. It is therefore of the utmost significance that even this last absolute in which man, particularly man in his technical state, has placed so much confidence, should today have been shattered, and that this should have happened, not on the ground of apologetic designed to safeguard theologically the reality of God, but through the progress of natural science itself which has brought us to the point of a serious dispute between determinism and indeterminism within physics and biology.

Let us once more look back over the chain of argument by which we have reached this conclusion. We started from the fact that it belongs to the fundamental structure of our whole polar existence that only what is past and has happened stands unconditionally fixed, and that on the other hand everything which has still to be includes a component of uncertainty. Here it is enough to recall the example of the Krupp steam hammer. Next we traced the various ways in which men have essayed to overcome this uncertainty in respect of the future, or at any rate to minimize it. The causal-mechanical world-view of Laplace is the most prominent of such ways, followed by Hume's account of causality, and finally by Kant's impressive attempt to deal with the causal character of the world process by reference to the *a priori* conditions of thinking. All these human attempts at a solution brought us in the end to the mighty saying of Christ upon which they break as the waves of a stormy sea break upon a rock. This divine word of power is summed up in the majestic saying: 'If you have faith as a grain of mustard seed, you shall say to this mountain: Remove hence to yonder place; and it shall remove; and nothing shall be impossible unto you.' Here we are confronted with a statement such as we could never have expected and which is quite incredible from the human standpoint. In the omnipotence of God it lifts from their hinges all human attempts to resolve the problem. Let us be quite clear as to the significance of this word of power. This does not lie in the fact that some unnatural energy which an extraordinary man might have as a potential power within himself came to the point of expression at a particular place in the world. To understand the precise bearing of the saying it is of the greatest importance to notice that Christ said: 'If you have faith as a grain of mustard seed' then the tremendous things of which I speak will happen. The 'grain of mustard seed' does not suggest a tremendous charge of power comparable to any kind of earthly energy such as that which develops in an atomic bomb. This seed is a tiny, almost a microscopic object, which, according to the biological notions of the time, carried no hidden power in itself. When therefore it is said that faith as small as a grain of mustard seed (which therefore a very feeble man is capable of having) may release world-shaking effects, this incredible and incomprehensible saying must carry the sense that the greatness or the smallness of the thing in question here does not affect the issue. In respect of quantity it is not commensurable with earthly things. All that matters is that the thing Jesus is talking about should actually be there. In line with all that has been said in this book, we can give an account of what it is that Jesus is talking about only in these terms: To have faith does not mean to be in possession of any kind of peculiar source of power, but rather to have access to another sphere which lies beyond all earthly powers. Any one of us may either have this access in its entirety, in which case all the possibilities of another world are open before him, or the access may be entirely closed to him. Jesus says about this that if you have faith, then nothing will be impossible to you. For in that case you live under quite different conditions and possibilities. You stand, if one may so put it, in an entirely different space, with a completely different basic structure from that of polar space in which we are at present enclosed. What Jesus is talking about becomes intelligible only in terms such as these. Here He is speaking about two conditions in which it is possible for us to be, and both of them, if we are in them, govern our whole thinking and living. The first condition, from which Jesus separates Himself and proposes also to liberate His disciples, is the one which Luther indicates by the translation 'doubt in our hearts'. The Greek word ($\delta\iota\alpha\kappa\rho\iota\theta\hat{\eta}\ \acute{\epsilon}\nu\ \tau\hat{\eta}\ \kappa\alpha\rho\delta\acute{\iota}\alpha$: Mark 11.23) has a wider range than this. It denotes a cleavage within the heart, in virtue of which we are pulled first to one side and then to the other. The condition which is meant here can be expressed in terms of existentialist philosophy provided that we use what has been said earlier about the fundamental law of our polar existence. This existence fundamentally rests on a continual unresting rhythmical motion to and fro, since only what has happened has certainty whereas everything which is about to happen is loaded with uncertainty. This restless rhythm of all events finds its existential expression in the fact that in virtue of respect for the uncertainty in what is to come, our basic attitude (*Grundbefindlichkeit*) is dread, fear and anxiety. The desperate fear of the disciples during the storm on the lake, when they cried in anguish: 'Lord, save us, we perish!', offers an impressive picture of this human situation. Something utterly astonishing follows upon this cry of despair. The Master, who hitherto had been sleeping peacefully, stands up and without for a moment losing His peacefulness gives the order to the raging sea: 'Be quiet and hold your tongue!' What is remarkable is that He uses no magical formula and makes no attempt to bring any kind of special power into operation. What He does reminds one, both in manner and tone, of an officer giving an order to his men, knowing that he can rely unconditionally on their obedience. In former times there was a well-known command which played a considerable part in exercises and manoeuvres: 'Company Halt!' referring to everyone engaged in the exercise. When this command was given, together with the signal for obedience to it, the entire exercise came to a dead stop instantly. That is how we are to picture what happened when Jesus, standing on the prow of the ship, ordered the breaking waves to stop. The eye-witnesses of this event were left with the impression that one who could do that is able to give the order 'Company Halt!' not only to the waves, but also, when the time is fulfilled, to the whole world-process which surges around us, and to do it from the other dimension from which He comes. This is the point of the incredulous comment: 'Who is this? Even wind and sea obey him!' (Mark 4.41ff.). He seems to come from another world which exists under entirely different conditions from our own. The same character of ability to command is there in all the other instances where Jesus confronts natural forces or persons possessed by demons as a commander. 'Stand up and walk', 'Lazarus, come forth'.

Under all these words we are aware of the calm of a commander who has complete power. They all lead us to the decisive question: What does it portend when Jesus sets the word 'faith' against the swaying to and fro of human doubt, the wavering which peculiarly expresses the fundamental character of this polar world? What is the significance of His saying: 'Whoever does not doubt, does not waver, but believes that it will be done, to him nothing is impossible'? What does Jesus mean by the word 'faith', the thing which according to His own words unleashes all the powers of heaven? The term is not used as yet directly in reference to God, as it is in the sentence 'Have faith in God' which occurs in the same context. It has first an entirely general meaning which we must grasp clearly if we are to proceed from this to achieve understanding of belief in God. The word 'faith', which so far we have been using in a particularized way according to the contexts in which we have found it to occur, can be given a quite general exposition in terms of existentialist philosophy on these lines: Faith occurs where an absolute is given, taking 'absolute' in the sense in which it has been used in all four sections of this book. Where, for example, absolute matter is accepted, then, as we saw, there arises faith in the absolute object. Where, as in the case of Newton, an absolute space and absolute time are taken to lie at the foundation of all scientific calculations, there arises faith in the absolute space and the absolute time. Where, in some form or other, a causal necessity is postulated, whether of the causal-mechanical kind or after the manner of Kantian Transcendentalism, there arises faith in the absoluteness of the causal nexus. We can therefore say quite generally: Faith is the relation of my *I* to an absolute, whether merely assumed or real. This absolute may have an entirely theoretical character, as in the instance of absolute space and absolute time which Newton used to underpin his calculations. It may, however, be of a more practical character and exercise a particular and decisive influence on a man's life, as in the instance of faith in the causal-mechanical world-view. In either case we may call the relationship in which my I stands to such an absolute a 'faith'.

Having got past these introductory general remarks we are in a position to make intelligible what Jesus and His believing disciples meant, and still mean, by the word 'faith'. We may sum up everything that has emerged from these four sections where we have been engaged with natural science by saying that in each of the four spheres which have been under discussion, natural science confronts an absolute. These absolutes have suffered a disastrous blow, not as a result of human speculation, but through the progress of scientific work itself. Each is threatened with collapse. The consequence of such a collapse must in each case be a return to faith in God as the sole being which has genuine absoluteness. All other apparently absolute magnitudes are like idols whose altars are on the verge of collapse. The faith which is relevant in this situation has therefore a negative and a positive side. To come to God we must first decisively repudiate all apparent absolutes, let them go, break our faith-relation with them. But this is only the negative presupposition of faith in God. Now comes the positive aspect upon which everything turns. We must yield ourselves to God, the true absolute, with our whole heart, and commit ourselves entirely to Him in theoretical as much as in practical respects. The way to faith is therefore composed of two actions, both of which are necessary if the goal is to be reached. The first action is the abandonment of all absolutes in which hitherto we have sought anchorage. Looking back over the development of this book, it appears that the first such absolute to which we have been committed is material property. How frequently has it happened in our time that a prisoner returning home has discovered that all the worldly goods in which he had trusted had become a pile of rubble! Yet it is this abandonment of all our former material possessions which for us is the way to God. The second absolute to which we have given our hearts is the sense of being at home in absolute space and absolute time. Thousands are finding the way to God today through the fact that they are compelled to leave behind the security of home and wander homeless in foreign places. The ьnird absolute we must leave behind is reliance on the technical (including the medical) causal nexus. For many people the way to God takes them through a tremendous disillusionment in respect of the faith they had had in widely known medical authorities. The way to faith, for these people, involves leaving behind the confidence they had had in the infallibility of contemporary medical science. In all these examples we see that the way to faith is bound up with a great inner peril. The danger lies here, that the person involved has to leave behind all his former assurances without knowing whether or not he will find a new anchorage. This may be seen in the behaviour of those men who can most obviously be reckoned men of faith. We recall the significant part played by temptation in the life of Luther, and the troubles which beset August Hermann Francke because of the great schemes of construction which he undertook in faith. It is clear too in the letters of 'Father Werner', written at the time when bankruptcy threatened him, when he kept the shining example of Francke before his mind but still the miraculous help for which he yearned so passionately did not come. These men found by experience that we have to do with a living God whom we cannot compel by our prayers if He Himself has not already made His sovereign decision. Prayer, in all these cases, became a perilous risk, a death-leap, whose outcome we do not have within our power. It depends entirely on God whether we, who have renounced earthly securities, are caught in the arms of God, or whether we crash broken to the ground. This is the second action involved in the way to God; the dangerous possibility with which we have to reckon. The way to God has properly been described as 'letting oneself fall', and has been compared with the first flight of a baby eagle, pushed out of the nest by its parents, and then discovering to its amazement that the invisible ocean of light in which it is dropping is capable of bearing it up. The presence of God which surrounds every one of my readers is like this invisible ocean which bears us up more surely than do all visible means of security. The marvellous peacefulness in God which comes upon us only in such a situation is the secret of all genuine acceptance of prayer. Jesus makes it

clear, in His saying about the removal of the mountain into
the sea in response to believing prayer, that this acceptance
has nothing to do with magic, black or white, but rests solely
on the fact that the man who prays becomes, at the moment
of his praying, an instrument of the active God in whose
hands he rests. We may recall the way in which Paul,
involved in a terrible storm at sea during his journey to
Rome as a prisoner, takes over the command of the threatened
ship, and tells the sailors and the soldiers who recognized his
supremacy what is about to happen, with an authority which
is divine.

V

THE PROBLEM OF MIRACLES
IN THE LIGHT OF
MODERN NATURAL SCIENCE

17. THE THOMIST CONCEPTION OF MIRACLES

It has become apparent in all that we have been considering that modern natural science, faced with the question of
what it is which moves the world process, has reached the
frontier of its possibilities of knowledge. The causal method
of enquiry comes to a halt at the threshold beyond which lies
the inner sanctum of what happens, the innermost events
from which proceed determinate effects out of which the total
process is built. Thus discussion of the old question of
miracles, which once occupied the foreground of the argument between science and religion, is set in a new context.
So long as the world-picture of Laplace held the field, where
each of the smallest particles of the world-machine had a
prescribed and invariable course to pursue, natural science
was involved in a life and death struggle with two attitudes.
The first of these was the conviction that there is freedom of
the human will, and the second was belief in a God who per-
forms miracles and answers prayer. The two attitudes are
intimately related. This is clear enough when one considers
how the human will, when firmly resolved upon something
and faced with insuperable obstacles, turns into prayer which
seeks to set heaven and earth in motion, and also how every
historical personality of notoriously strong will lives in the
faith that he is the instrument of God and that God will
overcome all the obstacles which lie in his path. Both the
belief in God and the belief in freedom of the will stand or

fall with the conviction that events are not absolutely fixed, but rather that the course of the world process can be altered by an unseen hand. Whether we are dealing with a man who, after a long inner struggle, reaches for his pen in order to sign a contract which will put him under heavy obligation for the rest of his life and does so although it was possible for him to refuse, or whether we are reckoning with God upsetting the whole direction of human history by sending a uniquely endowed man, we have to do with cases which come into unresolvable conflict with the deterministic outlook of the older natural science, where the track of every atom, the movement of every man's hand and the outcome of every battle which has ever been fought in the history of the nations could in principle have been predicted with the same certainty as an eclipse of the moon.

As long as natural science postulated a continuous causal nexus which excluded any freely governed power of will, there was no breathing space for belief in God except for those who dared, despite natural science, to claim boldly that the almighty God could at any moment tear open the causal nexus like a piece of cloth. The two attitudes were complementary, like the positive and negative of a photograph: a science according to which every event in the universe is caused down to the last detail, and a belief in miracles according to which God is able at any moment to break through the natural course of events which He has Himself set in motion. The action of God may then be compared to one of the great rotary presses used in the production of modern newspapers. They are so constructed that each sentence in the newspaper is fixed in advance and goes over the rollers unaltered if there is no interference. But if the editor decides that a particularly urgent paragraph must go in at the last moment, the rotating machine is stopped for a moment by pulling a lever. Then the new paragraph is inserted into the text and the machine rolls on once more. This is the version of miracles which was born out of the conflict with the causal world-view of science, and which can only be maintained by way of protest against the methods of natural science. This concept of miracles emerged for the first time centuries earlier than the rise of classical physics, for we find it in the medieval scholasticism of Thomas Aquinas at a period when Aristotle's causal theory was accepted in church theology and served as a starting point for dogmatic formulations. God is the *prima causa* and the First Mover who established the natural order together with all the *causae secundae* which maintain the world in its process. Should God wish to act in sovereign fashion, He proceeds to arrest the course of the world-machine through the *miraculum suspensionis*. Then He interferes actively and inserts into what is already there an interpolation which originates directly from Himself. This being achieved, He sets the machine in motion once again by the *miraculum restitutionis*. If God intervenes like this in the process of nature which science establishes, we have a quite unique chance of settling the question as to His existence. For either something happens which breaks the causal nexus and shatters the framework which is explicable in terms of natural powers and natural laws; and this provides our proof of God, whose existence as an almighty being able to take the order of nature off its hinges has been demonstrated experimentally. Or it may be the case that every alleged miracle is capable of explanation 'in natural fashion', and belief in God collapses. This Either/Or to which the Thomist conception of miracles leads has been given its classical poetic expression in *Uber die Kraft* by Björnson. Pfarrer Sang is praying in church for the miracle of healing which alone can save his sick wife, and Bratt opens the bedroom door through which the sick woman will walk if the miracle happens. 'This day,' says Bratt, 'is decisive for my life.' The whole problem of belief in God has been focused for him on the one question: Where is the miraculous power promised by God to those who believe in Him? 'If to this generation there is granted a miracle— one which the keenest instruments of doubt are incapable of dismembering—one of which it can be said that all who see believe—then it would be realized that it is not capacity for faith which is lacking but only miracles. If only a miracle were to happen now, in our midst, so tremendous that all who saw it believed! Millions would stream to the place—all who live in need and longing, the disappointed, the oppressed, the sufferers, would come creeping here each from his village, his hut, his bed, with the sick in the front ranks, to find the divine revelation. But they would not be the only ones. All who are looking for the truth on earth would come after them. First, those whose thirst for truth is most desperate, the greatest spirits and most profound and earnest thinkers. Their joy would be most radiant, their faith the most weighty. It is not the thirst for truth, nor the capacity for faith, which they lack, but simply and solely the miracle. . . .' Then follows the final scene where the sick woman comes out in her white dress, and all cry Hallelujah. The bells ring out. There is a jubilant power in the singing as though thousands joined in it. The sick woman stands still and stretches out her hands to the singers. Pfarrer Sang embraces her. Then she slips slowly down from his shoulder and collapses. It had all been a great deception. The breakdown of the whole earthly causal nexus, so desperately expected, had not happened. The whole thing was nothing but the product of nervous tension, and therefore something entirely natural.[1]

The question which lies at the root of Björnson's play dates from a time when nature was held to be an inviolable causal nexus, within which the living God is only able to manifest Himself by rending asunder the natural complex at a certain point. It shows clearly enough that the deterministic picture of the world and the Thomist concept of miracles are only two different modes of expression for the same attitude of mind. Both represent man in his solitariness over against a nature which is intrinsically foreign to him. As a voluntary being he has lost solidarity with it, so that it seems to him devoid of soul. Only where the revolutions of this soulless nature can be stopped is God able to act. Otherwise God remains hidden behind the cold necessity of the world process.

[1] Recent Catholic accounts rest on presuppositions similar to the ones we find exposed in this drama, e.g. Kaplan Fahsel's *Therese Neumann*, where the life of this recipient of the stigmata is told without any reliance upon a factual violation of biological laws. Opinion is divided about the explanation of the miracle of Lourdes, but compare the purely pathological version given in Schleier's book *Das Wunder von Lourdes*.

18. THE VOLUNTARY CHARACTER OF MIRACULOUS EXPERIENCE

The whole situation is fundamentally altered if the innermost processes of nature are not absolutely determined, but rather have a structure which is reminiscent of vital processes. The question from which Björnson's play arises is then falsely posed. This question rests on an Either/Or: either everything takes place naturally, the natural process develops soullessly according to eternal laws, in which case God remains hidden; or there is evidence of a divine will, in which case the causal nexus must be interrupted. This Either/Or can no longer be maintained. For the process of nature has assumed a form such that a divine will can stand behind it. A miracle, then, can no longer consist in the intervention of a will in the behaviour of a machine. A quite different interpretation is called for.

The question then arises as to what will be the significance of a miracle, seen from the standpoint of the present world-picture of physics? We will probe this question by looking at some well-known miracle stories where we have clear instances of miraculous events. Christ took a deaf and dumb man aside, put His fingers in his ears, spat, touched his tongue, looked up to heaven, sighed, and said to him: Hephatha! meaning: Be Opened! And immediately his ears were opened, and the bond on his tongue was loosed, and he spoke quite correctly (Mark 7.33ff.). Or take a story from the acts of the apostles. Peter said to a cripple: In the name of Jesus Christ of Nazareth, stand up and walk! And he took him by the right hand and helped him up, and the man jumped up, walked, leaped and praised God (Acts 3.6ff.). Or take the incident which had such a decisive effect on the life of Christoph Blumhardt. Blumhardt, according to his own account, went to visit the bedridden Gottliebin Dittus who was desperately ill and found her racked with convulsions. On sudden 'inspiration from above' he walked quickly to her, took hold of the invalid's rigid hands in order to hold them together, shouted her name loudly in her ear though she was unconscious, and said: 'Put your hands together and pray: Lord

Jesus help me! We've seen enough of what the devil can do; now we want to see what the Lord Jesus is capable of.' After a few moments the woman wakened up, and to the astonishment of all present the rigor had vanished. We do not get the impression, in any of these miracle stories, of an ingenious person stopping a machine in its full course by some kind of little lever, effecting a repair, and setting the machine off once again. Much more, in all these cases, are we aware of witnessing a conflict of wills. With the intervention of the power of faith, which lays claim on the whole person, an opposing will is beaten down after serious resistance, and there is a shout of joy like that of the victor after a fight. Think of the dramatic scene recorded in Mark 9. In the absence of Christ the disciples had tried to heal a possessed youth, and they had failed. Christ comes back and expresses the strongest emotion in the words: 'O faithless generation, how long must I be with you! How long must I put up with you! Bring him to me!' The interposition of faith by the disciples was too feeble to overcome this strong enemy. Then Christ Himself takes the field and settles the issue (Mark 9.18ff.).

Miraculous events of this character are only understandable on the hypothesis, to which also we have been led by the latest developments in physics, that the process of nature in its deepest essence is not a dead mechanism whose course is laid down in fixed terms, but that it is something which in some sense is alive; something which man may influence by the interposition of the will in the same way in which he can affect a human opponent. The invisible background of non-human events, upon which the power for miracles always seeks to establish its hold, is certainly something of a different order from our human experience of will. It may, indeed, be of many diverse orders of which we can form no idea, and to which we cannot even bring analogies from our human experience. The 'clairvoyant instinct' by which animals seem capable of making relevant calculations of a kind which would mean for men a wearisome process of reckoning is already an instance of something completely beyond our comprehension. Still less comprehensible is the hidden background of inorganic processes. We have no analogy for it within our world of human experience. Nevertheless, as we have seen, the all-embracing 'space of existence' (*Daseinsraum*) in which we stand as beings capable of will is one which reaches as far as this hidden background of inorganic processes. In our intimate conflicts with inorganic structures which daily life is always forcing upon us, we are inclined to the view that in the whole of nature forces are engaged and decisions are being made which must be similar in some way to our own acts of will, however different may be the form in which these decisions are made from the form of our own willing.

What follows from this in respect of our understanding of miracles? It is tempting, in view of the inexplicable and incomprehensible nature of miraculous happenings, to take such things with reference to some inner process, and to talk about them in much the same way as does E. Hermann, who claims to rely on Luther, or as Rudolf Bultmann does in his essay *Zur Frage des Wunders* (*On the Question of Miracle*), published in *Glaube und Verstehen* (*Faith and Understanding*, p. 221). 'To speak of miracle is to speak of my own existence; to say, in fact, that God has become apparent in my own life; and therefore to speak not of a general manifestation of God but rather of His revelation. If I see that God's hiddenness means that He is hidden from me, I also see that His hiddenness signifies my godlessness, my sinful condition. For He should not be hidden from me. There is only one miracle therefore, that of revelation. But this means forgiveness, revelation of the grace of God for the godless.' Anything beyond this falls, according to Bultmann's subsequent writings, under the heading of myth. But it is not enough for us simply to attend to this innermost point about the religious issue involved in God's revelation. The notion of miracle has a much broader sense. To grasp the essence of miracle we must not confine our attention to the religious man's experience of miracles. We must look also at the experiences of men in general which occur in the everyday life as well as in the magic of primitive people, and which recur, in another form, in the general course of our highly developed medical practice. There is something highly mysterious about the commonplace act of will whereby we order our hands to grasp a particular tool, and to carry out the hammer blow or the axe's stroke which we have willed, or to strike the keys of a piano, or to write a sentence on a piece of paper. Up to a point we are able to trace the course of the waves propagated within our bodies when the tracks of the motor nerves are stimulated from the cerebral cortex and the corresponding muscular reaction is evoked. But it is beyond our understanding to say clearly how this wave motion is initiated and from what invisible centre of command the order originates which our nerves and muscles proceed to carry out. Each of us, inasmuch as he is an active being, knows only the inner aspect of this objective process. If, however, we think about this inner happening standing behind the outward process which we are able to perceive, we stumble at once upon a fact which is of the greatest importance for the question which is here under discussion. If, as a healthy man, I give the order to carry out a particular movement to my hand or my foot, I know that the order will be obeyed. It is entirely obscure to me how I reach this assurance. It does not rest on the fact that I know about the physiological nexus which obtains as between the cerebral cortex and the movements of my limbs, and that I am convinced from experience that the channels of transmission are in working order and that therefore the instruction can be carried out. Unless I have studied anatomy, I have no notion whatever about these inter-connections. Nevertheless, knowledge that the order will be carried out is undeniably there. This certainty is like something granted to me from hidden depths. Only if the knowledge is present am I able to will, and to give orders to my members. If I entertain doubts as to whether my hand or my foot will in fact obey me, which is what happens in certain states of paralysis, I am able only to wish that the movement might happen, but am not able to will it. A person suffering from nervous paralysis says: 'I cannot get out of bed. I simply cannot achieve it because I cannot bring my will to bear on it.' We see therefore that the simplest motions in our everyday life rest, if one may so put it, on a faith which cannot see but which does not doubt. A masterly gymnastic performance, a virtuoso performance on the violin, or a moving discourse by a gifted orator are all possible only in virtue of a sustained effort of will which, on a basis of long practice, has become entirely unconscious and mechanical. There is no room for speculation as to whether what is aimed at will be successfully achieved. Such doubt must be eliminated. The complicated motions required can then be carried out with the certainty of a sleep-walker. On the other hand it may happen that a man begins to stammer at the very beginning of a sentence which he is uttering because he is assailed by doubt as to whether or not he will really manage to enunciate clearly one particular word. If this doubt can be cured by some technique of suggestion, and the stammerer comes to believe in his own power of utterance, then in very many cases his whole mechanism of speech is put right. In this everyday occurrence of the movement of our limbs, therefore, with its background of stimuli through nerve channels, we are already confronted with the mysterious fact which Jesus expresses vividly in the general statement recorded in Mark 11.23: 'Truly I say unto you: Whosoever shall say to this mountain, Bestir yourself, and throw yourself into the sea! and shall not doubt in his heart, but shall believe that what he says comes to pass, he shall have it.' Jesus does not say that a particular man can transfer a mountain into the sea by uttering a magic word. He merely says that if every trace of doubt has been banished from the heart in respect of some event, then that event will take place. Clearly no one could utter such a ridiculous command without feeling doubt about its fulfilment. But it is precisely upon this 'not doubting' that everything depends. In other circumstances, where doubt could be completely banished, success would not be lacking. For indeed the certainty we enjoy in respect of everyday behaviour is only possible because we are reaching out into the dark future with a clairvoyant assurance that what we resolve upon will indeed happen. This is the inner structure of every act of will. Now, however, we have reached the stage where organic processes within the body other than the motions evoked by the motor nerves may be effected

through this 'believing and not doubting'.   Modern medical
experience shows that this is the case in respect of processes
which previously were thought to be influenced only by
medical treatment, baths, rays, injections and operations.
This mode of influencing organic processes within our bodies
comes down to the fact that I must believe and not doubt
that the adjustment which is required will in fact take place.

How is this 'believing and not doubting' to be achieved?
The means adopted in medicine is that of 'suggestion'.
'Suggestion' is simply a term to denote a process which cannot be fully accounted for in objective terms by which we are
led, not from outside by any kind of external medical manipulation, but from within, to believe and not doubt that the
effect which is being sought will in fact supervene.   For
example, a person under hypnosis may be told that he has just
been stung by a wasp.   A swelling corresponding to a wasp
sting will then appear on his skin.   Blisters may be produced
by the same means.   Stigmatization is a recurrent phenomenon in the case of certain people who have special aptitude to
receive it in the course of profound meditative inner absorption with the event of Christ's crucifixion.   Wound marks
appear on their bodies, and in some instances the wounds
began to bleed each Friday.   The stigmata of St. Francis of
Assisi were at one time dismissed as a mere legend.   But in
recent times there have been other instances which have
served to convince us of the factual truth of this wondrous
event.   The nun, Anna Katharina Emmerich, born at Dülmen
in the county of Münster in 1774, whose story was beautifully
told by Clemens Brentano, had a vision when she was kneel-
ing before a crucifix in the Jesuit church at Coesfeld.   The
heavenly bridegroom came forth from the shrine and handed
to her the crown of thorns.   As it was placed on her head she
was conscious of severe pain, and later the places on her head
which it had touched were bruised and swollen.   The
stigmatization which followed was accompanied by great pain
at the points where the marks were imprinted.   The case of
Therese Neumann of Konnersreuth, and the other recent
case observed in his own house by a medical man, Dr. Alfred
Lechler, seem to be similar.   The other well-known fact

which lies on the same plane as stigmatization is that women are able, under suggestion, to produce the swellings associated with the condition of pregnancy. Similarly, significant changes in the foetus have been evoked by means of influences brought to bear on an expectant mother. There was the case of a young mother who was visited frequently in the second month of her pregnancy by a friend who, through some accident, had a distorted finger-nail which resembled a lion's claw, on the index finger of her left hand. The mother fixed upon this deformity and was possessed with the notion that her child might be born into the world with such a finger-nail. And that indeed was what happened. In his book, *Das Wunder in der Heilkunde* (*Miracle in the Art of Healing*), Erwin Liek has described 'irregular miracle healers' such as Zeileis, Coué, Weissenberg, Kneipp, Felke, Rasputin and others, and other less notable instances of people without any medical training who nevertheless had an extraordinary power of suggestion and were able to achieve cures which were beyond the scope of academic medicine and all its resources. Zeileis, a famous healer at Galspach near Linz, cured cases of tuberculosis, cancer, epilepsy, diabetes, arteriosclerosis, blindness and paralysis. It is clear, therefore, that it is 'not merely "nervous", but also organic illnesses'—i.e. not merely psychopathic functional disturbances, but also anatomical afflictions —'which are open to be influenced in psychic ways'. The external means employed, a gadget which Zeileis carried in his right hand and which was connected up to a high voltage electrical source so as to produce wonderful blue flashes in the darkened room, was not, in the judgment of medical observers, employed to produce a true medical effect from outside, but was merely superficial trimming 'which could be dispensed with where necessary, or replaced by some other externality'. It was therefore a means by which to reinforce the mass-suggestion brought to bear on the hundred to a hundred and thirty people who assembled at any one time in the darkened room. 'The real magic was in Zeileis the man', in that he understood how 'to create around himself a sphere of confidence'. 'But the point of attack,' Liek concludes, 'is not the sick body; it is the sick soul.'

The case of the French marine, V. L. of Rochefort, which was written up by Th. Ribot in his collection of pathological-psychological studies, (*Les maladies de la personnalité*, Paris, 1894), contains what is perhaps the most astonishing organic effect ever achieved by internal rather than external means under close medical scrutiny. He was the illegitimate son of a notorious slattern, and was soon sent to the St. Urbain training colony. Working there in the vineyard, he once grasped a snake which was hidden in a bunch of grapes. He was so terrified that he had a stroke, followed by a second, and then by paralysis of the lower limbs. It was eventually decided to train him to be a tailor. During his apprenticeship he developed a placid and grateful character, and genuine remorse for his past life. Then he had another hysterical epileptic attack which lasted for fifty hours and ended in peaceful sleep. When he wakened up, the paralysis had gone, and with it his new placid personality. The old violent criminal type was back again. He broke away from the colony, joined the marines at Rochefort, was imprisoned there because of a robbery he had committed, and in the prison he had another very severe hysterical epileptic attack. He was under observation by two doctors, Bourru and Burot. There it was shown that it was possible to transfer the condition of paralysis from one part of his body to another by devices such as the imposition of iron or steel appliances, particularly when magnetized. The differing states of paralysis corresponded always to different personalities, with distinctive characters and inner attitudes. It occurred to the doctors to try and reverse the process by influencing directly the patient's spiritual condition in order to induce a corresponding physical change. The attempt was astonishingly successful. The doctors hypnotized the patient, and he was told: 'V., this time you will waken up as a tailor back at Bonneval.' When he wakened up he believed that he was in the tailor's workshop, and he had his former placid character. But at the same time he had the former kind of paralysis where half his body was bereft of sensation. The same kind of experiment was successfully performed in respect of all his other states of consciousness. This case, so carefully observed, shows clearly that it is possible not merely to put a man into a certain spiritual condition by physical influence affecting his bodily condition, but also, as both doctors said in their combined report, 'to perform the experiment of inducing a corresponding physical effect by influencing the spiritual condition'. This 'influencing of the spiritual condition' means in every case achieving in the consciousness of the patient a conviction that a certain physical condition will supervene, or that it already obtains.

How may a conviction of this kind be evoked in the mind of a patient? By means of words spoken to him, either in his waking state, or, as in this case, when he is under hypnosis. But the important point is this, that the power which proceeds from these spoken words does not have its root in any physiological effect, i.e. any direct stimulation of the waves of the sensory nervous system. If that were so, it should be possible to use a gramophone record instead of the living voice of the man who utters the words. The power of the words resides entirely in the inner disposition of the doctor from which the words emerge. If suggestion is to be successful, a certain prerequisite must be available. In ordinary external medical treatment, the personality of the doctor is of relatively slight importance. The doctor is able to confront the patient as an objective observer, with an attitude of detached neutrality, much as the technician confronts the machine in which he has to effect a repair. But in the case of influence by suggestion, matters are quite different. Here the doctor, or the 'irregular healer', must give full play to his personality. 'The one who is treating the case must be firmly convinced that the treatment is going to succeed.' Only if that is so can he 'rouse the Psyche of the invalid, and make the sub-conscious soul receptive to the order which is coming to it by way of the cerebral cortex'. The treatment rests, therefore, on a basis of 'the irrational, of the doctor's faith in what he is doing, and of the patient's faith in the healing art and healing power of the man to whom he has committed himself'. The thing which cannot be fully probed scientifically is the way in which the doctor who makes the suggestion reaches this condition of faith, and how it is that the faith then leaps across to the patient like an electric spark. Liek can say no more than this: 'Beyond question, there are men who give out power', 'dispensers of power' to whom may be applied what is said of Christ in the Gospels: 'And all the multitude sought to touch him, for power came forth from him, and healed them all' (Luke 6.19). Other men, and Liek counts himself as one of them, are quite simply unable to get to the point of believing and not doubting. And of course it is precisely those with good scientific training who find it much harder to shake off their scepticism than do the naïve laymen. They are generally to be found, therefore, in the ranks of those who do not give out power, but rather absorb it, and 'to a certain extent may be said to live parasitically on this psycho-spiritual level'.

Parapsychology attempts to explain the way by which this faith secured against all scepticism is achieved, by reference to 'the sub-conscious', a stratum deeper than that of consciousness which is susceptible to doubt. Impressions can be made upon this 'deep soul' by the method of suggestion, almost as though it were a sensitive wax plate, and these produce changes within the organism. Oskar Kohnstamm, who in 1900 founded a sanatoria where observations covering periods of many years were carried out in this field, distinguished three levels of the sub-conscious: one of experience, one of ordering and the most deep sub-conscious. This most deep sub-conscious is the supra-individual underground layer in which the 'I' is embedded. It is therefore free from all that is personal. It corresponds to what Kant had in mind when he spoke of a 'consciousness in general', a 'pure subject of knowing'. It is 'the great I' into which, according to the teaching of northern Buddhism, the small individual I disappears like a summer cloud into the blue of heaven; the trackless original ground into which the mystic plunges in meditation. To explain his success in healing, Coué did not require several levels of the sub-conscious. He was content with a single deep stratum which he distinguished from the conscious will. This he called 'the unconscious' which rules all our organic activities. He cites the example of a girl who had had a tooth out, and instead of any attempt being made to stop the flow of blood by physical means, she was told by him: 'In two minutes the bleeding will stop.' The effect was punctual to the second. 'How are we to explain such a thing?' Coué asked. 'It happens perfectly naturally. Under the influence of the notion "this bleeding should stop", the unconscious gave the order to the affected veins and arteries that no more blood must be allowed to flow away from them. They compressed themselves obediently, therefore, just as they would have been compressed by the application of an artificial means of stemming the blood, as, for instance, adrenalin.' By a similar order, passed on by the unconscious, it is possible, according to Coué, to cure constipation, various forms of paralysis, tuberculosis, wounds and tumours. The arteries go on strike at the command of the unconscious and the tumour dies, withers up and disappears, because its means of nourishment have been cut off.

Whether one assumes a single 'unconscious', or whether one assumes a whole architectonic structure of many storeys, this kind of assumption does not afford a complete explanation of the puzzling fact that an 'order' is given to parts of the organism which cannot be reached through the system of motor nerves, the effect of which cannot be disturbed by doubt, as is usually the case with conscious decisions of the will, and that this order, which carries its own assurance of success, will in fact be carried out. All that such assumptions do is to translate the fact into a form which is more or less mythological. If a distinction is made between the upper storey of the consciousness, and one or more underground cellars, this is merely a parable in terms which can be envisaged, drawn from three-dimensional corporeal space. But all the resources of Euclidean stereometry will not enable us to penetrate to the secret of what confronts us here. The facts, as they are disclosed, belong to another order of things, which has to be distinguished as the non-intuitive space of existence from the intuitive space. These spaces, however, as we have seen, do not fit together like a series of cellars which are separated from the ground floor by a staircase. They are 'dimensionally' separated from one another.

The cases which have just been described show plainly that

alterations can take place within the human body to a quite extensive degree, which are not induced from outside either by stimulus of the nerves or muscles, or by the effect of medicine, but solely through certainty about their successful achievement.   Liek, who is a doctor, ventures to write this far-reaching sentence: 'There is no functional disturbance in the living organism, no illness, whether we call it functional or organic, which is not amenable in a greater or less degree to influence brought to bear on the soul.   This, to take a most grim example, is true even of cancer.'   In principle, therefore, no limits whatever are set here to the spiritual influencing from within of the processes of illness.   This fact has a liberating effect, especially when one considers the paralysing effect on the soul of an invalid of the thought, characteristic of the age of causal mechanism, that the infirmity must take its course through his body with the unalterable necessity of a machine, that he is caught and mangled in its merciless wheels, and that there remains nothing for him to do except to watch the process of the disease helplessly and resign himself fatalistically to what cannot be helped.   Now at last we are able to break free from the overweening power of this causal-mechanical picture of nature, which works on suffering people like a 'bad suggestion', and hinders them from bringing their spiritual power into action against the disease.

There is one more thing to mention.   The effects which proceed from this mysterious factor which is indicated by the phrase: 'believe and do not doubt that it will happen', are not confined to the limited region of our own bodies.   A remarkable number of well-attested experiences point to the fact that influences originate from this inexplicable source of power which reach far beyond the body of the man who experiences it, and produce changes in organic and in inorganic bodies at a considerable distance.   It may in fact show all the signs of 'action at a distance'.   The best known and most widely attested of these instances are those where a person, say a soldier who falls in battle, seems to get into contact over a vast distance with his nearest and dearest in the moment of his death.   This may happen through some kind of appearance or vision.   In that case one may venture to suggest that the dying man himself does not participate with his will in the event but that the recipient of the manifestation perceives what happens by some kind of clairvoyance (cryptaesthesis) or telepathic 'second sight'. This account breaks down in cases where it is not a vision or audition, i.e. an inner experience of the recipient, which mediates the impression, but rather an alteration in some inorganic object, for instance a picture falling from the wall or a clock stopping. There is a well-attested case in the Black Forest where the clock chain suddenly snapped and the weight fell with a crash to the ground, leaving the hands pointing to a precise minute. This minute, as was established a few days later, was exactly the one at which the father of the household died many miles away from home. Among the Indian fakirs there are some who can produce effects of this kind at a distance by concentration of the will which they have developed over a long period of training. There is also the case of 'healings at a distance', practised regularly at one time from a centre in Hanover, which essentially consisted in careful training to produce the conviction that the healing would succeed. Father Ivan of Kronstadt was well known throughout Russia because of his power to heal at a distance. One well-attested instance of his effectiveness dates from October 1889, when two children contracted diphtheria in a certain household. The disease rapidly took a serious turn, and the decision had to be taken whether the operation which is done on the windpipe in desperate cases ought to be performed. The worried parents telephoned first to Father Ivan who was in Kronstadt several hundred miles away. He received the message before the morning service, and at once concentrated his powers of faith upon the healing of the two children. At the very time, nine in the morning, when he did this, the doctor who was at the children's bedside in Moscow noticed a quite unexpected improvement in both patients. At two in the afternoon, when the operation was due to be performed, he declared that it was not necessary. And in three or four days both children had recovered. (D. Vorwerk: *Gebet und Gebetserziehung*, 1913, Vol. I.)

Many such well-attested cases could be quoted which

demonstrate in an unprejudiced fashion that effects can proceed from the concentrated will irrespective of the distance involved. In this context it is not our purpose to review cases of this kind. We are concerned only with the fundamental thesis that already the concentrated will can in fact overcome spatial restrictions, and that this is even more apparent with faith free from doubt. In everyday practice, relatively narrow limits are set to this action at a distance by the will. For always it is only specially gifted personalities who emit influences of this kind. But the effects achieved by these 'dispensers of power' sufficiently prove that such invisible action at a distance is a possibility, and that we are entitled to assume it even where we have not perceived it. It is readily to be understood that such effects are independent of spatial separation if we may take it that the will does not belong to the realm of perception, but rather to the second space which we have previously distinguished from the space of intuition and have called the space of existence. This space of existence has no internal frontier with the space of intuition, as though it were a neighbouring room separated from one we can see by a wall. Rather is it equally present at every point of the space of intuition. Spatial limitation therefore does not apply to it.

What is the bearing of all this on the question of miracles? The facts we have adduced show that it is incorrect for us to suppose that the 'faith which moves mountains' is a characteristic specialty of certain experiences where supernatural powers are at work of which no account can be taken in ordinary life. It is already the case that every movement carried out by our hands or our feet in response to an order from the will is, when looked at from within, a faith lacking sight, by which we know in advance by a clairvoyant certainty that successful obedience will follow. And to this faith, as we have seen, no limits can in principle be set. Not only can it produce alterations within our body, but also it can reach beyond our body and overleap spatial intervals. This faith belongs obviously to the inner structure of the whole world process, which lies hidden behind its objective superficial aspect. Thus the contrast often drawn between natural and supernatural events must be abandoned, for everything happens naturally. The miracles of the fakir, the miracles of medicine and scientific healings at a distance are all natural. For they express the inner structure of the world process. On the other hand, it is equally true to say that everything is miracle in so far as we experience it from within. For the fact that faith reaches out with invisible hands into the dark future is always beyond understanding and we can only contemplate it with wonder. If this is how matters stand, we can obviously no longer contrast miracle and the causal nexus, at least in the way that contrast has hitherto been drawn. If a general distinction is still desirable between miracle and natural happenings, then the distinction must be put upon a new basis. The impression given by the most remarkable instances of action at a distance by the faith which moves mountains, does not carry us beyond a merely relative distinction to be drawn between everyday powers of the will and extraordinary demonstrations of power which may occur by the concentrated willing of specially gifted personalities. We can move beyond this relative distinction only on the assumption that, beyond all the relative magnitudes and limited powers available in this world process, there is an absolute magnitude. The one absolute magnitude which lies beyond all relativity is the almighty God whose sphere of power is not limited, as is that of a god or demon in heathen polytheism, but who is the absolute total sovereignty which governs all that is and all that happens. As long as we leave out this absolute God, then the most abnormal event which seems to break all the laws of nature and to require a suspension of gravitational powers or of the principle of energy is only a very impressive and hitherto unobserved instance of the invisible power exerted by the concentrated will. Matters will be different if God, as sole Lord over all powers, emerges from the darkness in a way we cannot prescribe, and establishes contact with us. The magical hinterland of the world-process was much more directly accessible to primitive man than it is to technical man of modern times. The world-view of animism, which seems to have prevailed at some time in every part of the earth, was a mythological expression of

primitive man's profound insight into the powers of will
which stand behind the process of nature, and of his attempt
from the very beginning of his existence to become a vehicle
of this power of will, and thus to take advantage of its unseen
forces.   Thus arose the fear of demons, and the magical
invocation of spiritual powers by means of a developed
practice of magic, which we find in all peoples.   The enlight-
ened man of our technical epoch has dismissed this as laugh-
able superstition.   In truth, however, it is simply a mythical
attempt to give expression to the very real inner aspect of
the world-process which we have been discussing.

19. THE SIGNIFICANCE OF GOD'S SELF-REVELATION FOR MIRACULOUS EXPERIENCES

When God advances out of the darkness as sole Creator
and Lord of all powers and initiates His conversation with
men as 'the first and the last, the one who is and who is to
come, the almighty', an unpremeditated light falls upon the
magic twilight which surrounds the penetrations of primitive
man to the hinterground of the world.   The world's morning
dawns, the light is divided from the darkness, and this unexpected event, which can only originate from God's side,
brings a division of the spirits.   For if *one* God is the power
present everywhere throughout the world, no power which
has the character of will, wherever it acts or holds sway in the
world, can remain neutral in relation to Him.   All powers
are summoned to decision for or against the one who has
emerged from His hiddenness to take command over them
all.   Therefore for every being endowed with will which
co-operates in the shaping of the world there are two, and
only two, possibilities.   Either it acknowledges its lord, and
becomes an obedient organ of the one to whom alone it pertains to command.   Or it ventures to resist him and to rebel
against him in Promethean pride.   A fierce battle thus ensues.
The powers of will which refuse to be subordinated to God
fall prey to the demons.   Their cultus turns into heathenism.
Any attempt which men make to lose their selfhood in a
medial relationship with divine beings, so as to propitiate the

power of these beings and turn it to advantage, becomes at once something which is very far from harmless. It turns into 'black magic' and the practice of devilish arts, leading to an uncanny dependence upon dark powers and the loss of community with God. For in relation to the eternal Thou who now has confronted us, there can be no practice of magic. In relation to Him it is not possible to dissolve into some mystical twilight-state. Only one relationship is possible with such a Thou. It is that of personal dialogue between I and Thou, in the waking attitude of prayer. Once this new state of affairs has been set up, something which can only happen in virtue of a sovereign self-communication of the sole Lord, it is at last possible for miracle to be invested with its original biblical meaning and its distinctive significance. In the Bible, the miracles wrought by God never stand in opposition to laws of nature or to a causal nexus. Wherever the Bible speaks of the natural order it emphasizes its regularity as something ordained by God and as expressing the fact that God emancipates man from chaos and grants him an 'order' in accordance with which he can direct his life and work. Thus after the chaotic calamity of the Flood, God promises to those whom He has saved to be a kernel of a new humanity, that 'while the earth remaineth, seed-time and harvest, cold and heat, winter and summer, day and night shall not cease' (Gen. 8.22). In Jeremiah, the cosmic orderliness of the stars is taken to be an expression and a parable of God's faithfulness towards the people whom He has entrusted with a special task: 'Thus saith the Lord, which giveth the sun for a light by day, and the ordinances of the moon and of the stars for a light by night, which stirreth up the sea that the waves thereof roar; the Lord of hosts is his name. If these ordinances depart from before me, saith the Lord, then the seed of Israel also shall cease from being a nation before me for ever' (Jer. 31.35ff.). Because the rules which govern the process of nature are divine 'ordinances of preservation' in virtue of which an ordered human life in community is alone possible, the law of nature and the divine action can never come into conflict in the Bible. Nowhere in Scripture is the causal nexus treated as the antithesis of miracle. The antithesis of miracle is something quite different. The significance of miracle comes out of the new world-condition which begins when God emerges from His hiddenness as the sole bearer of total sovereignty over all that happens. Miracle is the mighty act in which the one God confronts the demonic powers which seek to maintain themselves in opposition to Him despite His self-revelation. The essence of miracle is seen most clearly, therefore, at the moment of world history where an actor is found upon the stage who, unlike all the others, remains wholly obedient to God, 'obedient to death, even to death on the Cross'. Christ, as the plenipotentiary of the one God, had the task of defeating the demonic powers which are defying the sole sovereignty of God within the human and the extra-human world. These powerful wills are ranged, according to the biblical view, under the control of a single unifying will whose goal it is to dethrone God and to destroy His creation. This will to destruction does not only operate in the terrifying form which obtains where men are directly taken into possession by demons and lose control of their own bodies and, in this state of possession, are caught up in constant convulsions and inflict upon themselves grave injuries. The Satanic will to destruction lies also behind the whole range of sicknesses which distort the human body and slowly destroy it. Christ knew Himself to have been sent in order to quell the entire rebellion stimulated within the created order by the opposing power. In Acts 10.38 this significant aspect of His mission is indicated quite simply by the words: 'He went about doing good, and healing all that were oppressed by the devil, for God was with him.' Because God, the Lord of all, was with Him, because God stood behind Him as the one who laid upon Him His task, He was from the outset more than a match for all these powers of will. Jesus is 'stronger than the Strong One whose demonic fist beats down on all the world and all its history'. 'The demons know at once who they are dealing with and what awaits them, just as a prisoner recognizes the executioner and knows all too well who he is' (E. Stauffer).

Since the demonic powers' will to destruction lies also behind sickness, Christ, as the one who is stronger than the

demon world, is able to lift the curse which comes upon a
man in his affliction. He therefore heals the crippled woman
who had 'a spirit of infirmity', meaning a demon, which had
caused her eighteen years of suffering. Jesus says, according
to Luke 13.16: 'Ought not this woman, being a daughter of
Abraham, whom Satan had bound for eighteen years, to have
been loosed from this bond?' But it is not only behind
organic suffering that we find demonic powers which must
submit to Christ. Inorganic powers of destruction, such as
the stormy sea which threatened to annihilate the disciples,
have also a demonic background. Christ confronts them with
'the lordly invective of God, to which there is no answering
back and no defiance'. He says to the sea: 'Shut up! Be
quiet! And the wind ceased, and there was a great calm'
(Mark 4.39). In all these cases, the miracle does not lie in the
suspension of natural necessity, but neither does it lie merely
in the believing subject's inner experience of the forgiveness
of sin, though this supreme experience of God's grace is part
and parcel of the greatest experiences of miracle. On the
biblical view, nature is not subject to any fatalistic determination which calls for suspension by a miracle. Seen from
within, nature is a war of living powers of will. In the case
of a miracle, a higher will intervenes in the conflict of living
wills. God encounters the destroying powers which permeate
the created world. At one particular point he already accom-
plishes what will be the case all along the line at the world's
consummation: the restoration of the original order of
creation, where there were no destroying powers, and where
the form of the world had not yet assumed its present death-
ridden character. At present, however, this happens only in
isolated instances. All we can say at present is that mighty
acts happen here and there which serve as great signs thrust
up to call the attention of those with eyes to see them to the
supremacy of God and of His plenipotentiary over the world
of demons. Since in the Bible the process of nature is not a
causal mechanism the interruption of which may be demonstrated objectively, it is not possible, on the biblical view, to
find in miracle an experimental proof of God's existence.
Where the demons are still in power, they too can produce

miracles and extraordinary signs. Already in the Old Testament we find it explicitly said that a miracle does not authenticate the divine mission of a prophet. 'If there arise in the midst of thee a prophet or a dreamer of dreams, and he give thee a sign or a wonder, and the sign or the wonder come to pass, whereof he spake unto thee saying: Let us go after other gods, which thou hast not known, and let us serve them; thou shalt not hearken to the words of that prophet' (Deut. 13.1ff.).

So long as we have not yet been encountered by the one God, the Lord of all powers, so long therefore as our eyes have not yet been opened to perceive the complete power of His Christ, we are not yet able to distinguish between a mighty work which takes place in the course of the divine operation and a demonic work of magic. We lack the relevant criteria. Everything which we have adduced so far goes to show that all extraordinary works of power take place in the same form. They all occur in conjunction with an inexplicable faith, free from doubt, that what is believed will surely happen. Faith, in this general and formal sense, is therefore not a distinctive criterion. It belongs to the inner structure of the act of will. The difference between divine miracle and demonic magical power first begins to appear when we raise the question as to how this mysterious certainty which is free from doubt comes about, or, to put it more precisely, whence it is that a man derives the inner legitimacy of reaching out into the darkness of the future with unconditional certainty. For to do so is not possible beyond all further question. That is why the High Priest and the Sanhedrin put the question to Peter and John when they had miraculously healed the lame man: 'By what power, and in what name have you done this?' (Acts 4.7). The Jews knew that demons could perfectly well be driven out by the authority of Beelzebub. Their expulsion, in itself, does not necessarily bespeak divine authority. It is also possible that a man may perform miracles in his own name, that is to say, by a concentration of his own will and by faith in himself. This appears clearly in the dangerous consequences which follow upon all healings of this kind performed by strong-

willed men. Those who are healed come at once under the
hypnotic influence of the healer. They are not able to get
away from him. The moment he comes within range of them
they experience the uncanny sensation of being under his
power. It is only when God has encountered us personally,
and we live with Him in the fellowship of prayer, that we are
able 'to discern the spirits'. Then we are able to trace at
once whether the healing power under whose influence we
stand comes from below and therefore makes us dependent
upon men or upon demonic powers which draw us away from
God and hurl us down into awful depths of godlessness, or
whether this healing power comes from above and brings us
into closer relationship with God and deepens and strengthens
our fellowship with Him in prayer.

To illustrate this fundamental point about biblical miracles
we may quote two further reports of miracles from our own
day, both of which are well documented. The first one shows
the power of prayer in a conflict involving organic suffering;
the second shows the same power in conflict with inorganic
substances which threaten human life. The first report is
taken from the letters and diaries of Marie Hesse, the mother
of the poet Hermann Hesse. In 1894 she wrote: 'On June
2nd, Dr. Zahn told me that I was suffering from a disease in
the bones, but as my relatives wanted a second opinion I went
to consult Professor Liebermeister in Tübingen on June
20th. He confirmed what Dr. Zahn had said, and prescribed
a six months course of treatment for me: complete confinement to bed, daily baths, cod liver oil and sulphur. When
the six months were over, I showed no improvement. On the
contrary, indeed, the illness seemed to worsen; the pain and
swelling in my limbs increased, and every bone ached.' In
December, Dr. Zahn tried a course of treatment with phos-
phorus and with electrical massage, but it was of no use. The
report for 1895 was: 'Throughout the whole of this year I
was ill, miserable and confined to bed.' Then came 1896,
when she wrote: 'Schrenk came to visit us on January 4th.
During the night I had a discharge of gall, and pains in the
back. Schrenk said that up to now he had not felt that he
ought to pray for my health, and that I must become in-

wardly certain about the will of God. That He who had called Lazarus from the grave could cure me was not in doubt. He who had created the bones could easily heal them in spite of all that the doctors said.' January 11th: 'In the evening I asked Herr Schrenk to lay his hands upon me, in order that I may suffer quietly and patiently and glorify God to the very end.' Sunday, January 12th: 'Before eleven o'clock Herr Schrenk came, laid his hands on me, and prayed on my behalf for spirit and for power, and also quite suddenly for my recovery: Lift her up! Put her on her feet! I shrank back trembling. What was this that he was praying for! Was I to return to everything that I had abandoned as gone for ever? Then at once there came the thought: If God wants this, is my unbelief to prevent him? No! Lord, I will what thou dost will! And suddenly I had courage and joyful confidence to pray with him for my recovery. In spite of my discomfort the pains abated, and I was able to sleep that night like a child. I told this to Schrenk, and he said with great gladness: Now at last I have rightly had courage; we will pray together again this evening. That evening he again put his hand on me and engaged in heartfelt believing prayer. I felt something happen; powers flowed over me. That night I could not sleep for praise, thankfulness and joy. It flowed through me like a warm stream, pulsing from my head through every limb. I was able to give thanks for my recovery before I had even tested whether or not my diseased feet would bear my weight. I made a light and tried to get out of bed, holding on to the bedstead and the bedside table. I succeeded. New life and new powers were there for me. I could lift my feet again. Previously I had only been able to shuffle them when someone supported me. Although I had not slept for joy, I was bright and free from pain in the morning. When Adele came in, I asked her to dress me, for the Lord had made me well. She fell on my neck and wept. Then she helped me into my clothes, and led me to a sofa in the dining-room, next to my bedroom. At supper time, when I was still on the sofa, Herr Schrenk said he would rather I were at the table. I stood up, and came and ate at the table with the others. This was on Wednesday, January 15th, an unforgettable day in my life. I could move from one room to another, and my limbs moved freely. All my pains had gone.'

The biblical authenticity of this healing is particularly clear from the fact that it involved no exercise of concentrated human will. In the prayer which led to the sudden change Schrenk had no previous intention of asking for healing. For the patient, too, this development in the prayer was completely unexpected and overwhelming. The conviction that he must pray not merely for patience in suffering but also for recovery came to Schrenk quite unexpectedly from within during the prayer.

In this case, as in most cases of miracle and of answered prayer, what was involved was an organic process, and the intervention of a healing power which gave a new turn to the process. Let us therefore also quote a second miracle story from recent times, which has the same excellent documentation, but where it is an inorganic event which is given a particular turn by invisible powers. It is the story of the accident at the well in Ponickau (Saxony) in 1866, which is still remembered in that village, and about which we have a detailed written account from the pen of the village pastor at the time, O. Th. Auerswald. At the beginning of December 1866, a well was being dug to provide water for the village, and the shaft had to be excavated in sandy soil. Water was found eventually at a depth of twenty-three yards, and then, on the afternoon of Saturday, December 8th, the sand strata collapsed and buried the workmen, all of whom were good and zealous members of the congregation. The pastor, who had encouraged the best men in his congregation to work on the well-project and who felt a measure of responsibility for it, hurried off into the forest to get help from the water engineer who worked there, called Mahnert. In great inward distress he asked himself as he hurried through the forest: What is God wanting through all this? Then suddenly the saying 'Fear not, only believe' (Mark 5.36) flashed clear and bright through his soul. The case seemed to be utterly hopeless. Mahnert, when he visited the site, explained that to dig the sand out would take six or seven hours, and that in any case he could not begin on it until dawn the next day. While the work was proceeding on the Sunday morning, the pastor prayed in church with his congregation for a deliverance. 'Hitherto,' he said, 'when I prayed in church for earthly things, such as rain, I prayed in conditional terms: Hear us, if it pleases thee! For I thought that God may well wish to chasten us by means of a long drought, and those who are weak in faith may be offended. But this time I said: The Lord must help, according to His promise, that everything which in prayer you ask to receive shall surely be done to you. I pleaded His promise before Him. Call upon me in the day of trouble. We are in terrible trouble. Now, Lord Jesus Christ, keep thy word and show thy power. Let the buried men be brought forth alive and undamaged. If thou wilt hear and answer, we will praise thee and turn to thee with all our hearts.' In the course of the following day, two men came down from the mountains, and a second water expert, all of whom declared that the men were certain to be dead, but that they would help to dig out the bodies. Then there was a heavy downpour of rain and of snow; a pond collected in the village, rainwater poured into the shaft and carved out its own drainage. There was no possible ground left for hope. The pastor experienced a dreadful depression, and the congregation began to show its hostility to him. By this time it was Friday. Then Böhmig, a builder, volunteered to help on the work, in order to give the men who had worked for him from time to time a regular burial. He sunk a caisson and took responsibility for all the dangers. The pastor could not get away from the thought that no one could prove to him that the men were not alive. Preparatory work for the new excavation lasted until Tuesday, December 18th. Then on Wednesday the 19th, a week and a half after the accident, a cry suddenly rang through the village: They've found Zimmerman, and he's alive! Soon there was another shout: The others were alive too! The bucketfuls of sand flew into the wind. A happy, joyful silence settled on the villagers standing round the excavation. 'To me,' writes Auerwald, 'it was as though I stood by the grave of Lazarus and heard the word: Lazarus, come forth! At seven in the evening the great moment arrived. Traugott Muschter, wrapped in towels and blankets and tied to the rope, was lifted into the bucket, hauled to the surface, and taken off to bed. "Oh!" he groaned, "this is a different kind of bed from the one we've had under there!" Then came Wilhelm. He said nothing, while the crowd sang "Now thank we all our God" with hushed voices. How had it happened? At the moment of the accident they collapsed into each other's arms and in the tremendous din they lost consciousness. When they came round, they found themselves in a cavity. They struck a match, and saw that the collapsing baulks and planks had created a kind of hut around them, which was slowly filling up with sand until one of them managed to wedge a loose plank into the opening. The little hut was blocked at the top by a baulk lying askew across it. It proved to be remarkably firm, but very small for the job. There was a little sand-bank in the middle which one of them could lie on while the other crouched at his feet. They had no food, but they had a few fingers of brandy in a small flask. From the 9th to the 11th they felt neither hunger nor thirst. On the 12th they began to feel an awful thirst, and their fingers stuck to their gums when they put them into their mouths. They prayed desperately for water. And suddenly they heard it: drop, drop. . . . The rain was their salvation. They caught the first drops in their mouths. Later they stuffed paper into the bottom of a pipe bowl and used this to catch the precious drops. Thus they drank, day after day, until on the last day the water began to peter out. They consoled themselves with the thought that God would not have built their little hut for them and supplied them with water if He wasn't going to help them out. Then came the rescue.'

Looking back on the story, the wonderful event resolves itself into a series of wholly natural happenings. The movement of the sand strata, the downpour of rain—both took place according to the principle of gravitation and the law of action and reaction, in a perfectly natural fashion. Nevertheless, no one who went through that experience was able to regard it simply as a fortunate coincidence of accidental circumstances. They were all convinced that an invisible hand had been 'steering' these physical and chemical processes, and that the course of events was intrinsically related to the prayers of those involved.

And now, in conclusion, an episode from the *Memories and Experiences* of the Schwabian man of God, Seitz, which brings out clearly the inner connection between external miraculous happenings and an alteration in the inner life of persons involved:

'A young man, who had himself experienced an act of God in our house, brought to us a man who had been crippled in both feet for the last six years. When he was working on the railway, a rail had fallen on his back, and had damaged the spinal nerves in such a way that both his legs were paralysed. He told how the doctor had sent him round to various hospitals and spas, but in the end had said that he was incurable, but that if he lived in a place where the air suited him, he could prolong his life for a couple of years. So he came to us. I discovered at once that he was a man of integrity. A few meditations which he attended roused him so much that he undertook a complete purification of conscience and mind, and put right all that troubled his conscience. Wherever he had caused offence, he sought pardon, and where necessary he made restitution. The basis of this honourable integrity was undoubtedly his ability to believe the Gospel and the promises with childlike simplicity and joy. This gave me the pleasure, after a few days of his being in our company, of laying hands on him and praying for him. When we had prayed, he stood up on both feet and said: In the name of Jesus I am healed. And he began to walk about in his room, and in the dining-room which was next to it. Then he sat down, and wept for joy, and said: Ach, God, what have you done to me! I am really cured! The other guests were coming in for supper. Because the man had previously been carried to and from the table, they were astonished to see that he could now come to the table himself. He was so moved with joy that he asked them to permit him to tell them what the Lord had done to him, for they had seen how he had had to be carried about and now was able to walk for himself. After supper the guests gathered round him and asked him more about what had happened. He said that while praying he had felt the power of God, and had heard the command: Stand up and be healed! On his return home, he was for ten years a living witness to the Lord. He did much work for the Lord in his neighbourhood. He was often away for hours at a time, leading meetings. He founded a temperance union, and built community houses, until, serene and at peace, he was called from his labours.'

VI

THE RIDDLE OF LIFE

20. THE NON-OBJECTIVE BACKGROUND OF THE OBJECTIVE WORLD

If we look back over the conclusions which have been reached in the three previous sections, we see how it has become clear to us from one side after another why natural science, at the highly developed stage which it has now reached, stands at a frontier of its theoretical possibilities. This awareness of a frontier does not arise from the fact that there are further regions which must still be regarded as *terra incognita* for whose illumination we need better microscopes and better telescopes, nor from the fact that future generations of specialized research workers must continue to collect observations and make experiments and draw conclusions. Such a frontier of knowledge would be purely relative, and with each year it would be broken through. The frontier of which we are now aware is an absolute frontier, imposed by the nature of the case. It arises from the fact that the whole of exact natural research, with all its appropriate methods, lies within the limits of a particular space, within which all being and all happening must be ordered and beyond which we cannot see and shall not be able to see, even though the mirror of the latest American telescope were capable of reflecting all the spiral nebulae in the universe or if the latest electronic microscope should reach down to the as yet unattainable molecular dimensions. The only space which can be brought within our field of view is the space of objectivity. And our own existence, from which we cannot escape, reminds us every moment that the space of objectivity is only a partial aspect of the world and that reality has other sides of which we cannot give an objective representation. This other side of the world is too near to us for us to be able to stand away from it and bring it into focus on the photographic plate of our world-picture. And yet we know of its existence. We are entrusted with it as directly as we are with everything that enters into our intuitive picture. This non-intuitive space chiefly relates to the place where I myself stand, when the objective world in all its measureless expanse unfolds before my gaze like a brilliantly coloured panorama or an exciting film. This place is, at the same time, the point of origin from which I am able to intervene responsibly in the small area of reality which is open to my influence. The objective space has thereby come to receive an invisible foreground, a region from which it is visible much as a lighted stage is visible from the auditorium. But to this invisible foreground of the objective world there is also added an invisible background. For, in dealing with my fellow men, I am driven, as we saw earlier, by inescapable analogical reasoning to the hypothesis that my fellow men are not soulless automata. It is plain, on the contrary, that behind the objective appearance of their bodies, which is all that I am able to perceive, there stands an ' I ', which is no more perceptible than my own ' I ', but which stands in the same relation to the body which is sitting before me and speaking as does my ' I ' to my body. Thus, with all the techniques of natural science which are available to me, I cannot discover a single clue to the existence of this knowing and willing ' I ' which belongs to my fellow man's body. To take an X-ray of his body, or to operate upon it and lay bare its inner constitution and submit all its parts to microscopic examination, would be of no avail. I should never be brought to entertain the idea that behind the cerebral cortex and the electric currents which it radiates through nerve channels to the muscles over a system which extends to the furthest parts of a flesh-covered skeleton there may be something other than all that is directly observed and that enters into an anatomical analysis. I have this notion because, at the one point where I can see directly into the invisible background of the world —the point at which I myself act and suffer—the invisible ' I ' which eludes every category of medical research is given to me as a reality which is more real than all visible corporeality.   Therefore, if I wish to avoid the 'toll-house point of view' of solipsism, which is so alien to reality, I am bound to conclude that behind the outward show offered to me by the body of my fellow man there is an inward spectacle analogous to my own 'I', even though it is hidden from my observing eye.   Once I have drawn this analogical conclusion about my fellow men, I shall be further impelled, as we also saw earlier, to regard animals also, and indeed all organic beings, as something other than soulless automata whose existence is exhausted in their objective outward show.   These beings would not be engaging in such a desperate battle for light and air and living space against their enemies, had they not been placed, as I have, by a necessity of destiny which arises out of non-perceptible depths, in a position which they are obliged to defend even as I am obliged to defend my own. I must therefore suppose that there is an inner life behind non-human organisms, one which is indeed utterly different from our human thinking and willing but which, when it comes to the crucial point, has something in common with us. But now, because, as we shall see in a moment, it is suggested by the present state of research that there is an equivalence of structure between single-celled organisms and the molecules of the physicist, of a kind which eliminates the difference between the organic and the inorganic worlds, the 'principle of continuity' suggests the idea that an inner life may stand behind the elementary structures of inorganic reality, one which is still further removed from our human life of soul than is the inner life of plants, but one which we must assume to be there if the parallelism between an objective outward show and a non-objective inner spectacle is not to be broken at an entirely arbitrary point.   If we follow this line of thought to its conclusion, we shall come to the hypothesis that the world of objective space, which is the object of attention in natural science, has not only an invisible foreground, viz. the unobjectifiable 'I' which observes the brightly lit film of objective reality as from a darkened seat in the stalls, but that it also has an invisible background.   This will be the inner life which we are driven to postulate behind the outward show, which alone is visible, of both organic and inorganic processes.

If this is correct, then we must extend to the whole visible world which is the object of scientific research the kind of relationship in which we stand to the corporeal expression of life made by our fellow men. Fundamentally we stand in the same relationship to the whole of reality as that in which we stand to the visibly expressed life of our neighbour. We are quite unable to penetrate to the interior of another man. This is the root of all misunderstandings and of all the cruelties which we inflict on one another. But of course the whole physical appearance of the other man, his words and expressions and bodily movements, form a visible medium through which we are able to come into relationship with him. To illustrate the point we might use a parable which recalls Plato's allegory of the cave. Two subjects who confront one another are in fact invisible to each other. They cannot communicate directly with one another, however keen their desire to do so. A white screen hangs between them, of the kind used for shadow theatricals. They are cut off from one another by this screen, and neither can see the other. The stage behind the screen is illuminated and the screen is translucent, so that the movements performed by the one actor cast a shadow on the screen. In the shadow pictures thus thrown on to the screen by one subject, the other subject recognizes projections of the first, who is invisible. The first subject can therefore make himself known to the second by means of these projections. They are also the media by means of which one subject is able to affect the other. The white screen, by means of which such invisible beings become indirectly visible to one another through projections on a plane surface, is the space of objectivity which belongs to our physical world. But in place of the plane surface we must substitute the whole of three-dimensional space, which is where projections of our invisible beings may appear. This space is the battle field on which imperceptible subjects such as we are cross swords with one another and fight out all our desperate battles. In every encounter between man and man, whether it is a discussion in which two speakers engage, or whether it is a fight with machine guns and hand grenades, there are three magnitudes involved: (1) my own imperceptible 'I'; (2) the medium of objective space which hangs between, like a visible yet transparent screen; (3) the invisible other, with whom I have to deal, and who is trying through this medium to affect me and to bring me under his influence. This is the situation we are in, in all our daily dealings with our fellow men. Now if it is not merely human bodies which have such an inner side, but also animals and plants, and perhaps even molecules and atoms, we must draw this important conclusion: fundamentally we stand in the same relationship to the whole of reality as that in which we stand to our fellow men; and this is true even when we try, vainly, to portray to ourselves the inner life of the non-human world which may well lie behind its objective outward aspect. It is often said that when we are dealing with primitive organisms, such as the amoeba for instance, 'there can at best be an apathetic soul-life' only, compared with our human consciousness. Such contemptuous observations mean that we have already transgressed the limits set for our human experience. For it is precisely the simple forms of life which continually surprise us by their so-called 'instinct', in virtue of which they are able to carry out activities with the certainty of a sleepwalker, whereas men so poor in instinct as ourselves would need to resort to mathematical calculations and technical devices in order to do the same things by very roundabout methods. These instinctive abilities are as incomprehensible and astounding to men as our methods of building steam engines and aeroplanes apparently are to animals. The 'restitutions' done by a simple organism when it has suffered injury are much more perfect pieces of work than all the operations of highly developed human surgery. The provision made by insects for the care and nurture of their young, and the measures which they take against dangers which may threaten their offspring are far in advance of the most far-seeing welfare politics of men. May it not be that behind all this there is brilliant pre-vision and clarity in planning, in contrast with which our own wearisome calculating human understanding appears like an 'apathetic' state of consciousness? In any case, these things go to confirm our impression that the whole objective world, and not just the corporeality of men and animals, has behind it a non-objective background. At each point, objective space is a transparent screen, with an imperceptible being appearing through it by means of shadows, and manifesting itself more or less clearly through the visible medium.

From this point of view the limits of natural science which have appeared in the course of the last three sections become intelligible. Research which is directed exclusively to what can be established objectively is bound to overlook two magnitudes which belong to the very substance of reality as a whole: the invisible foreground and the invisible background. All that it can take into account is the third magnitude, stretched between these two like a visible screen which carries projections from both sides. What comes into our field of view is thus an abstraction which holds together the two realities belonging necessarily to the total picture. This brings us at once to a frontier of knowledge at two distinct points. The first point is revealed by the question: What is the object of natural knowledge? What is the essence of the world's substance? What is matter? If we abstract from the invisible background which manifests itself through the medium, the question about the deepest essence of the reality we have to do with can never be really answered. For always we see only the frontal aspect which this reality presents to us; the background remains hidden. We are sharply reminded of this when matter, the fundamental element to which we are led by objective contemplation of the world, itself becomes a problem for scientific theory, since it has been shown not to be something at rest in itself and existing through itself but rather to consist of fundamental particles whose continual transformations work out the effects of causes unknown to the particles themselves. At this point, therefore, we begin to feel that in matter something is manifesting itself which is not accessible to any objective observation. The second point where the limit of objective natural knowledge must be admitted, has to do with the relationship between the objective picture of nature and the invisible foreground across which it necessarily comes into our field of vision. Once the process of research destroyed the absoluteness of measurement and related motions, science was obliged to take seriously the mystery of the 'placing' by 'destiny', whose origin lies in unknown depths, but apart from which all our measurements and calculations remain relative, and which serves to supply us with an origin of perspective for our world-picture. Thus both the foreground and the background which enclose our objective picture of nature have come to be taken seriously. From these two points there arises a third where we know ourselves to stand on the frontier of objective study of nature. We feel the presence of the frontier when we regard reality not simply as a static picture but rather as a flux of situations and therefore as something which is happening. The question arises whether the course of events is fixed once for all by some determination, or whether it is an interplay between various possible tendencies which contribute to what shall be. As long as we remain unaware of the invisible background of reality, and therefore think that we have probed the world to its roots by getting down to fixed fundamental particles, what happens will seem to us to be a causal mechanism whose details can all be calculated and where the various parts move like wheels in a thoroughly intelligible clock. The Laplace picture of causal predictability expressed in the strongest possible form the sole sovereignty of the objective attitude to the world, in which both the invisible foreground and the magic glimpse into the invisible background were ruthlessly eliminated from the mind. But as soon as the firm bricks which had been taken to be the original components of the world-stuff dissolved into interchangeable systems, we found ourselves standing at a third point on the frontier of natural knowledge. For the fundamental processes, from whose cumulative effects the whole of macroscopic events are built, turned out to be something a-causal, something beyond the range of scientific explanation, arising from invisible origins and backgrounds.

21. THE PROBLEM OF A MECHANISTIC OR A VITALISTIC
    INTERPRETATION OF THE PROCESS OF LIFE

The frontier-consciousness awakened at these three points
by the present mature state of natural knowledge comes to an
inclusive focus when we speak about the secret of life, a
mystery which hitherto has offered insuperable opposition to
all attempts at a scientific explanation or at a physical and
chemical analysis. First we must ask in what relation does
the riddle of life stand to the three unsolved mysteries, which,
according to our exposition, mark the limits of natural
science? Is it a new problem which we are facing here, or
does the question about the essence of life hang together with
the three questions we have so far picked out, namely: What
is matter? How does the reference system arise? What is
the power which moves the world-process? The mystery of
organic life-processes tends, in most expositions even today,
to be clearly distinguished from the puzzles which we have
so far discussed. In the controversy between the mechanistic
and the vitalistic interpretations of life, which moved into a
new stage with the 'neo-vitalism' of Hans Driesch, it is supposed by both parties that the living entity with which biology
is concerned is in any case, in the first instance, something
utterly different from the 'dead' stuff of which minerals
consist. The question always comes down to this, therefore,
whether we must introduce a special factor to explain the new
thing which we see in the living cell, namely its so-called
'life-power' or the entelechy, as Driesch calls it, following
Aristotle, or whether this new thing can be traced back to
laws and energies which are there, though in simpler form, in
'dead' matter as well.

Now the change in natural science which we have met in
the field of physics leads at this point also to a fundamentally
new attitude. It undermines the significance of the whole
question which is at issue between the two trends in biology.
The battle between mechanism and vitalism only has a clear
meaning when there is a clearly understood distinction between dead stuff and organic life, that is to say, between the
basic parts out of which are fashioned the wheels, gears and

shafts of a machine, and the basic elements out of which a living cell is built. A profound alteration has come about at this point through modern chemistry and atomic research. First, we must leave completely out of the picture the 'inner life' which may stand behind organic and inorganic processes. We must attend simply to the outward picture which is all that can be observed objectively. Chemical investigation of the structure of materials yields the surprising fact that the stuff of which the world is built is not a homogeneous mass. It is granular in structure. It is disposed in separate structures which have a 'wholeness', each of which has an ingenious form which it manages to maintain. This special property of matter is most evident in the case of crystals. A piece of iron or graphite or diamond or calcium or silver or gold consists of infinitely tiny, beautifully formed, symmetrical configurations, in which the atoms are arranged so as to form cubes, octahedrons, dodecahedrons, etc. We can form some idea of the delicacy of these crystalline lattices by the following illustration. Think of a box whose volume is a cubic metre, its length, breadth and height being one metre. Imagine a set of such boxes stretching from Berlin to Cairo. Now compress the whole chain (stretching for nearly three thousand kilometres) into a millimetre; and if you ask what has happened to any one of the boxes, you have some idea of the size of the constituent elements in a crystal. Two million eight hundred and thirty-seven thousand of them go into a millimetre. That is the number of carbon atoms lying along the edge of a diamond cube measuring a millimetre. We can only explore this delicate structure of crystalline material by arranging for X-rays to fall upon it. The rays are deflected through the crystalline lattice. When the deflected rays are received on a photographic plate we have a spectogram from which we can deduce the form of the elementary particles. This is the so-called Laue-effect, named after Max von Laue. At first it may seem that our attention has merely been drawn to a single peculiarly brilliant art-form in nature, which occurs over a wide range of materials in the everyday world, but which offers no basis for conclusions to be drawn about the whole of world-stuff. P. Debye and P. Scherrer took up an isolated position, which has now been adopted and more securely established by F. Rinne, when they said that from a structural point of view 'there is no difference in principle between a crystal and a chemical molecule. Both have the characteristic property of containing atoms in a regular pattern. There is thus a fundamental general affinity of structure between atoms, molecules and crystals.' We may therefore work back from the crystal to the molecule where atoms are arranged in a pattern of wholeness; from molecules back to their components, the atoms, whose moving shells— 'electron envelope' or 'electron cloud'—lie symmetrically about the nucleus; and finally from the atom to the fundamental particles of reality, electrons, mesons, neutrons and protons, which exist in fixed quantum states. However different may be the forms of these elementary structures, they all have something in common. They exhibit a 'wholeness' which carries with it the power to retain a given form and to resist the destruction of it so long as they are not exposed to stronger powers which are able to dissolve the ties which hold their parts together. As we have seen earlier, atoms can be bombarded with rays and effectively disintegrated; they also can slowly collapse and therefore die a natural death. Just as organisms have a definite average length of life which is connected in some way with their inner structure, so certain kinds of atom collapse in a time which is prescribed by law. For instance, while thorium has an average life of $2 \cdot 2 \times 10^{10}$ years, there are other radio-active elements whose duration of life averages from ten to twenty years, and yet others which last only a matter of hours or even minutes.[1] While radioactive elements collapse for internal reasons, many minerals are exposed to destructive influences from an environment of air or moisture. The fact that tremendous energy must be brought to bear on the atom in order to force out electrons which are integral to it shows how strong a tendency must lie in the atom to retain its form in conflict with external disturbances. The struggle put up by these elementary structures on behalf of their present state and living space is

---

[1] The shortest average duration so far established is that of the boron isotope $^8_5 B$, which is in the neighbourhood of a trillionth of a second.

particularly clear when the temperature of a substance is altered so that the aggregate condition is changed, as, for instance, when a block of ice first melts, and then is turned into steam. H_2O goes through three stages: ice, liquidity and steam. In the solid state to some extent, and still more in the liquid state, the molecules are in movement within a certain field where they are loosely or elastically bound together. In the gaseous state this movement is enhanced until it becomes a 'powerful leptonic chaos. The particles move among themselves with the speed of bullets, each individual maintaining a straight course only for a very short period; they rebound from one another, shoulder one another out of the way, each one claiming a portion of the space for itself and around itself, the room which they aim at being the same for all gases'. Using Avogadro's Law, Loschmidt worked out in 1865 the number of particles in a cubic centimetre. At zero temperature and at atmospheric pressure, it is 27·6 trillions. In a volume of gas, therefore, there is a movement comparable to that in a thickly populated land where an enormous number of people have to live together on every square kilometre at very close quarters. If we touch a solid body with our hands and find it hot, as for instance a stone which has been lying in the sun, we experience something of the living movement in which the elementary particles of the body are engaging. The more deeply modern leptology (research into the delicate structure of materials) probes into these mysterious agitations and movements within the wholeness of individuals which make up so-called dead stuff, the more sharply we are faced with the question: Where is the frontier at which dead matter ceases and organic life begins? Is there after all a contrast between the dead and the living? We have been accustomed for most of our lives to the idea that there are three functions of the living cell which are lacking in dead material: (1) nourishment, and the growth which is connected with it; (2) propagation; (3) the capacity to receive stimuli and to react to them. It is becoming clearer every day that these three functions of life are also to be found, though in another form and on a much lower level, in the elementary particles of inorganic matter. The individuals of inorganic matter take to themselves material from their environment in order to increase their morphological unity. Further, they choose, just like living beings, what they will assimilate from their environment, choosing what is adapted to the building up of their particular form. This is most clearly to be seen in the case of crystalline lattices. A rock-salt crystal takes only the chlorine from its environment and rejects the alum substances which its neighbour needs for its growth. Among the crystals there are some which are omnivorous (biotite) and others which are epicures (quartz).

It may be suggested, however, that the mode of nourishment supplies evidence of a profound difference between the dead and the living. The organism grows by incorporating or storing the nourishing substance within its interior ('intussusception'). We think of the process of assimilation in plants, for instance, or in simple animals such as the amoeba. The inorganic structure nourishes itself by storing up or depositing material in its immediate vicinity ('apposition'). This distinction between organic and inorganic self-nurture is called into question once we penetrate more deeply into the mysterious process of crystalline growth. Crystals do not grow simply by external addition or deposits of new substance which resembles the old. At the surface of the crystal there is a delicate shell, distinct from the interior of the crystal. This 'crystal membrane' is so arranged that it is able to select, transform, attach to itself and assimilate material from the environment. Once the crystal membrane has fulfilled its task, it retires from the scene, and a new surface is extruded in place of the old one. This takes over the 'physiological function' performed by its predecessor. The whole process is strongly reminiscent of the skin-respiration in amphibia. The crystal membrane includes within its capacity for assimilation the power to transform and adapt itself when there is a change in the flow of nourishment in its vicinity. There are other inorganic structures which grow by 'intussusception' (the process characteristic of organic structures), as for instance bubbles of gas or drops of a molten liquid. On the other hand, there are processes of 'apposition' (characteristic of inorganic structures) to be found in the crystalline components of organisms, as for instance in the otoliths of fish or the cellulose in plants. The organic process of nutrition is not therefore clearly marked off from the inorganic. The two areas intersect.

Further, the fundamental organic process of propagation by division of cells has a preliminary inorganic stage, namely the formation of liquid crystals, which was demonstrated by O. Lehmann. Speaking of these bacteria-like liquid crystals, Lehmann said: 'The most remarkable thing is . . . that they are able, like bacteria, to divide into two or more parts which then behave like perfect individuals, continue to grow, and divide again.' According to F. Rinne, the separation is preceded by a change of structure where two cones of rays branch out from a point which becomes the point of separation, a process which reminds one of the plasma stars which occur in cellular division. Again, inorganic structures marked by wholeness are sensitive to stimuli and react to stimuli. This is demonstrated by elastic bodies, such as a spherical drop of water deformed by some mechanical pressure and resuming its shape when the pressure is removed, or a candle flame which flickers in the wind but resumes its former shape once the draught stops. More important than such elementary examples are optical effects which are evoked in precisely the same way in inorganic as in organic structures. The process of sight which takes place in the human eye, regarded merely from the external point of view and without respect to its inner side, is nothing but a photo-chemical reaction. This is evident from the fact that the film which covers the retina quickly loses its colour. Seen objectively, there is no specific difference between the process of seeing and the way in which the crystalline particles of silver bromide on a photographic plate react to the light photons.

We see, therefore, that the three most important functions of life, growth by nutrition, propagation and sensitivity to stimuli, have their preliminary stages in the inorganic field. If there is such an intimate fundamental relationship between the two natural realms, it is not surprising that we should come across intermediate forms which create doubt as to whether they should be reckoned to belong to the organic or the inorganic group. One such form is the virus which causes a disease of tobacco plants, the tobacco mosaic virus isolated by Wyckoff. On the one hand the virus is something that can be crystallized and preserved, and thus not something that would ordinarily be regarded as a living entity. It resembles the substance in the white of an egg and has a very high molecular weight, and if it is preserved in glass it retains for a long time its power to cause the disease in a tobacco leaf. The ultimate entities of which this virus-stuff is composed are clearly molecules. Stanley and Wyckoff have in fact shown that the individual virus is a single molecule with a molecular weight of something like two million five hundred thousand. Further light on the construction of these molecules is expected by the use of the electronic microscope. And yet these individual viruses have the ability of living substances to assimilate material which they need for their construction from their environment, and thus to increase without limit by using available material, though the ability is only exercised when they find themselves on a tobacco leaf where the tiny organism is able to find material to assimilate. Fifty virus molecules in a single plant cell are able to produce a remarkable effect. It is supposed, indeed, that because of its auto-catalystic mode of increase, this virus could destroy the cell completely. The virus, in fact, behaves just like the long-familiar bacilli which cause tuberculosis, the streptococci and staphlococci and so forth which have always been regarded as micro-organisms. We must therefore regard the virus individuals also as single-celled organisms.

The continuous connection between the inorganic world and organic structures becomes even closer if it can be maintained that the ultimate unities which are the bearers of heredity and propagation in all organic forms, the so-called genes, are single molecules, like the virus individuals, which react to X-rays and to ultra-violet rays in the same way as do other molecules which engage the attention of physicists. When the physicist Pascual Jordan expressed the view that the genes were molecules, the overwhelming majority of

biologists dissented.[1]   But as long ago as 1935 or 1936, Del-
brück, Zimmer and others brought forward new evidence
which went to confirm Jordan's view.   A gene seems to be a
single molecule containing somewhere between ten thousand
and a million atoms.   A particularly clear indication of the
molecular character of the gene is the fact that its changes take
place in accordance with the laws of quantum mechanics.   A
gene is capable only of variable changes.   Its mutations are
quantum jumps of the molecule, occurring either because of
the impact of an electron or because of absorption.   When
cells are killed by radiation, the same amount of radiation
produces varying effects.   This may be explained by the dis-
persion of the shots in consequence of the quantum character
of the radiation.   In certain cases it can be established that
a cell is hit by a single alpha-particle.   But on an average,
eight thousand shots are needed to give one which is fatal.
The others do no damage at all.

   All these facts, though still matters of investigation, already
show with undeniable clarity that the cleavage between
'dead' material and the world of life is one that has already
been bridged.   If we are looking simply at the objective outward aspect of inorganic and organic individuals, this is one
point that can be affirmed with certainty.   If we leave the
question of animation completely out of the picture, the
frontiers between the dead and the living worlds dissolve
away.   The contrast which has hitherto been assumed disappears into a hierarchy which ascends from simpler to more
complicated structures.   When we survey the incalculable
richness of nature, we see that all the forms which have been
produced in such immeasurable fullness, from electrons to
atoms and molecules, then to the macro-molecule of the cell,
and from there to the complex of cells which is the highly
developed organism, are all variations on a single theme, an-
nounced first by a couple of notes and then developed into
ever fuller harmonies and richer melodies.   The theme is
that of a self-contained wholeness, over which, like a leading
idea, there stands a characteristic form, which builds itself

   [1] It is not for us, as laymen, to take up a position of our own in the debate
about Jordan's hypothesis.   We may, however, report upon it.

up out of material from its environment, maintains itself by doing battle against all threatening disturbances, and multiplies itself indefinitely if no limits are imposed on its increase. In front of each natural entity there stands 'a picture of what it ought to be', a form for whose realization it strives with all its powers. The discovery that the gene, the unit of heredity, which contains potentially within itself a particular characteristic of the organism which is to be and transmits it from generation to generation, is a single molecule, prompted Pascual Jordan to ask: 'How can powers be released through this tiny single molecule which are capable of constructing and forming a whole organism?' We must not at this point pursue the answer Jordan gives to this question, because it is still hotly disputed.

22. THE EXPERIMENTAL SOLUTION OF THE PROBLEM OF LIFE

What is the effect of all this on the decision which has to be made in the old conflict between mechanism and vitalism, and therefore on the problem of world outlook which lies behind this struggle? To be clear about this, we must first glance at the present state of the conflict between these two tendencies. Then, on the basis of what we have just learnt, we shall be able to take up a position of our own. The old dispute has moved into a new stage today, now that the discussion is no longer in terms of natural philosophical debate, but rather an attempt is being made by tedious and carefully devised experiments to compel nature itself to give an answer to the question. Both W. Roux, the leader of the evolutionary-mechanical trend, and Hans Driesch, the founder of neovitalism, believe they have discovered a method of persuading nature by experiment to yield up what may be its last secret. Their considerations begin from the essence of a machine, say the clock in Strasbourg cathedral, or a bicycle, or a machine gun, or the mechanical equipment of a great factory. However different such machines may be, they have one thing in common. Each element in the complicated pattern of interlocking machine parts fulfils one and only one definite and limited function in the operation of the whole. It is indeed conceivable that, by some particular clever mechanism, one part might perform several functions at the same time. The ball-bearing case which surrounds the hub of a bicycle wheel serves on the one hand to ensure smooth motion, and on the other to help with the mechanism of the brakes. Even in such a case, however, the number of functions fulfilled by one and the same part is strictly limited in number. Each element of the machine, says Driesch, has one and only one 'prospective meaning'. Now from this statement about the structure of a machine arises the question which has to be put to nature if we are to know its secret; we find a clue to the kind of experiment which will induce nature to answer the question we wish to put to her. We must interfere quite crudely with the growing organism, or with the life of a completed organism, and see how it responds to such shocks. The question is whether it will behave like a set of machinery struck by a bomb at a moment when all the machines are running. In such a case the damaged parts stop working and drop out; other parts which have not been touched may go rattling away mechanically irrespective of whether they are producing anything or are running empty. Or is it the case that higher powers are at work in the organism which make up the damage in most remarkable ways? It would seem then that the question which must be put to nature is a simple one and that the answer should be a simple yes or no. But the odd thing is that nature does not give a simple answer to this clear question. It does not say yes or no, but yes and no. W. Roux inserted a red-hot needle into a frog's egg which had just divided to give two cells. He confesses that he did it with a secret shudder at his temerity in thus interfering with the secret life process of a living entity. The result was that half the egg died and the other half stayed alive. The surviving half went on growing and turned into a half embryo, the marrow of its back and the shape of its intestine being half of what would result from lateral division of a full embryo. Each element in the original egg seems therefore to have its limited 'prospective meaning' just like a machine part. This, therefore, was evidence for mechanism. H. Driesch allowed a sea-urchin's egg to divide first into two cells which he separated and cultivated separately; then, with another egg, he used four cells, and so on. The results were not half urchins or quarter urchins, but in each case whole ones. A complete form was developed from the separated parts so long as the division did not go beyond thirty-two. If one compares the tasks performed by a single embryonic cell, when the organism is allowed to grow undisturbed, with the tasks which the same cell is obliged to take over when it is isolated by this kind of interference, it is clear that one and the same cell can take over wholly different tasks in the building up of the whole organism should circumstances demand it. The same remarkable capacity for regeneration had been observed in plants, for instance in the begonia leaf which can be cut into any number of tiny pieces and yet the whole plant regenerates itself from such a bit; it has also been observed in animals, for certain worms have been cut into seventy-two pieces and each has generated a complete worm. The same thing is true of the polyp hydra which is less than a centimetre long and haunts our fresh-water lakes. They can be divided longitudinally, or by oblique sections, and reduced to quite tiny separate bits, and every section grows into a complete polyp provided that its length is not less than a sixtieth of a millimetre. Every such bit carries within itself the power to develop into a complete animal.

The capacity of certain organisms to develop their wholeness from a particular part can be demonstrated even more exactly than is possible with embryonic cells by experimenting on finished organisms, where the amputation of a part stimulates restitution of the missing part. It is true that all organic entities do not have this capacity for restitution. Birds and mammals hardly have it at all, and neither do men therefore. But other forms of animal life have it in very large measure. If a salamander loses a leg, another leg, with all the bones belonging to it, grows out of the wound. In the case of many worms, the head and the front part of the body can be cut off, and a new head grows out of the wound. This, indeed, may be repeated many times. Such 'regeneration of a regenerate' is a particularly astonishing sign of the inexhaustible life-power of nature.

This remarkable power of regeneration enabled H. Driesch to put in a more precise, form the question to which nature refused to give an unequivocal answer in the development of embryo cells. He put the question by making experiments with forms of life possessing the capacity for restitution, and the hydroid polyp *Tubularia* which grows on the bottom of streams was a particularly suitable object for such experiments. This polyp looks rather like a candle-stick, with a hollow stem three to five centimetres long and a head or hydrant. This hydrant at the top of the stem has a base surrounded by a crown of tentacles, and a funnel also crowned by a ring of tentacles. There are thus two crowns of tentacles, different in form and size, through which nourishment is drawn. If the head is cut off, a new one grows within eighteen hours, but not from tissues covering the surface of the wound. Soon after the section is made two separate rings appear on the stem, of a reddish colour, just below the wound, each composed of thread-like sections. The alteration takes place, in fact, in the undamaged part of the stem. The threads begin to swell and then split, and we have the makings of two new crowns of tentacles which, however, are still on the stem. The tissue between them expands and they are forced away from the stem to become a complete new hydrant. But now we come to the chief feature of this experiment. One might suppose that certain tissues were equipped to produce one part of the hydrant in case of emergency, and that neighbouring tissues were ready to produce the other part. In that case, restitution would take place at given intervals below the particular point where a section is taken. But the fact is that the precise tissue which produces the base of the hydrant and its crown of tentacles in one contingency is apparently able to produce the funnel and its crown of tentacles if the cut is made at a slightly different place. The cut can be anywhere you like, and the parts of the organism immediately below the surface of the section take over the tasks which are allotted to them in the particular circumstances.

What kind of answer is suggested by this fact to the question which is at stake and which is constantly being put to nature in the current discussion between mechanists and vitalists? The question is: Is life a kind of machinery, a blindly running causal-mechanical process, or is some autonomous life-power at work here which cannot be traced back to laws of physics and mechanics? It would seem that the answer given to this question by the processes of restitution is not an equivocal one. H. Driesch drew this conclusion from his experiments: If, in the restitution of the hydrant, each part could only assume one particular rôle, then the whole thing could very well be machinery, though of a tremendously complicated kind. But the fact is that any part you take is able, in case of need, not only to produce the whole, but to effect the reproduction of any of the parts. Therefore each element of the system must contain in tiny form not only the whole machinery, but beyond this must have potentially within itself any particular part of it. Since the point of section can be anywhere, there must be infinitely many sets of machinery, arranged at infinitely small intervals from one another, and therefore lying in such a way that only a space differential separates them. This means abandoning the whole notion of machines. A new natural factor must be operative here which is not localized at a particular point and operates only from there, as do the energies known in physics and chemistry. This new natural factor, on the other hand, must be equally present at every point of the whole organism, and it must consistently govern what happens within an organism.

23. THE PROBLEM OF TRANSPLANTATION IN THE GROWING ORGANISM

If all processes of restitution were similar in form to the typical cases upon which Driesch chiefly relies in his philosophy of the organic, the answer which nature gives to man's question as to whether or not we can explain organic life in causal-mechanical terms would be clear and unmistakable. It would be established in unbiased fashion that a factor is at work here which cannot be localized anywhere in the organism, but which transmits an order to any part of the system to do what is necessary in order to overcome the damage which has broken the structure of the whole. But Hans Spemann and his disciples have taken the lead in carrying out a whole series of careful tests on growing organisms in order to determine more precisely whether, at each stage of development, the capacity is there to direct the process of growth in accordance with the wholeness of the organism, and to rectify damage in a way which accords with the total plan. As a result it has been shown that the capacity to produce, at need, the whole of the organism or any particular part which has been severed, by way of restitution from a remaining part is not there throughout the whole process of development, but only at an early stage prior to gastrulation, the point at which the embryo develops, when the group of cells which previously had a mulberry-like formation (morula) forms into a hollow sphere (blastula) and then takes the shape of a cup (gastrula). When the organism has reached this stage, and a piece is cut off from it, what takes place is precisely what led W. Roux to his mechanistic theory of organisms. It is no longer the case that a whole embryo develops out of a half, but only half an embryo. 'Pluripotency', i.e. the capacity to produce one of several parts according to need, is not inexhaustible as it seems to be in the case of the tubularia or clavellina, but is limited by certain relations. It is there only in the initial stages. That the capacity for restitution in organic structures is quantitatively restricted, as though it were a kind of physical energy, is made particularly clear by the transplantation or grafting tests which Spemann made with salamanders and frogs. Such a transplantation is first made within one animal at an early stage of its embryonic development. The cells which later would go to form the tail are extracted from their original context and transferred to a place from which a leg ought to grow. From this group of cells, which would have gone to form a tail if they had been left in their original position, a leg is formed. At this early stage, therefore, the group of cells is still a plastic material which, just as in the case of the tubularia, is taken into the service of the wholeness-tendency, and adapted to the needs of the situation. But if the grafting is done at a later stage, the transmutation no longer takes place successfully.

The determination towards tail construction which this group of cells receives at its original place has become too strong. What happens is that a tail develops at the point of grafting although it is a highly unsuitable point at which to have one, and from the point of view of the total plan it is a ridiculous misconstruction.

The limitations which are placed on the wholeness-tendency become even clearer when the grafting is not done within one and the same organism but when groups of cells are transferred from one species of animal to another. Spemann grafted part of the group of cells from a salamander which should have formed its abdominal skin into the gastrula of a frog at the point where its mouth should be developing. The wholeness-tendencies of the two different kinds of animal came into conflict. It was as though stones from a Roman-esque basilica which had already received a measure of Romanesque ornamentation were incorporated into the walls of a Gothic cathedral, with the result that a compromise be-tween the two architectural styles appeared. What happened in this grafting was a compromise between the structural plan of the salamander organism and that of the frog organism. In fact what was produced, in accordance with the new context, was not abdominal skin but head skin. The frog organism was to this extent able to incorporate the grafted cells and use them as building material. But the transfer did not wholly succeed. Instead of the suckers which are found in the tad-pole's mouth which enable it to cling to water plants and make use of them, there appeared adhesive organs of the kind found in salamanders. Driesch's theory, that there is a mysterious natural factor present everywhere in the whole organism which forms and directs every part from the idea of the whole, received its worst blow, however, from Spemann's discovery that the capacity[1] to give a simple determination to cell material with the whole organism in view was not uni-formly distributed. This determination seems to have a point of origin, a basis of operations, or an 'organization centre'.

[1] These clumsy expressions for such a 'capacity' or 'wholeness-tendency' are evidently used by the author to avoid the danger of pre-judging the correct line of interpretation. Zoologists will probably think that the English phrase 'axial field' could profitably have been used.—(Translator's note.)

The closer a part is to this '*Urmund*', i.e. to the cells which form the actual cup at the gastrula stage, the stronger is the principle of construction imposed by their original context; the less likely is it, therefore, that these parts will be readily adapted to their environment on being transplanted. The further the development of the organism proceeds, the greater will be the range of this determining power which proceeds from the *Urmund* and which seems to have its original seat and organizing centre there. The limits beyond which parts can be found, which, on transplantation, will adapt themselves to the new environment are therefore set further and further back. The determining power behaves like a wave motion such as arises in a pond when a stone is thrown into it, and the ripples spread in ever-widening circles from that point outwards. When, for instance, H. Mangold grafted a portion of the *Urmund* of one gastrula into the womb of another organism, this portion, which would have later become abdominal skin, created an entirely new embryo of its own kind from the material of the animal into which it was grafted, that material being at that stage indifferent to any particular form. The cells of the *Urmund,* therefore, clearly have the power in themselves to impress the form of their own species upon the cell groups of an entirely different environment.

24. MECHANISM OR WHOLENESS-TENDENCY?

We see from all this that nature does not give an un-equivocal answer to the question which is put to her by renewed experiments in the course of the battle between mechanism and vitalism. The question is whether the organism is a machine in which each part is able to carry out only a limited task, or whether an omnipresent form endowed with will stands behind the organism and directs all the processes which occur within the organism. Must we therefore introduce an entirely new natural factor in order to understand organic life? The answer which nature gives to this question is an equivocal one. On the one hand we are confronted with a life power which under no circumstances can be explained in mechanical terms. On the other hand it seems that the new form-building power which we have come across is localized in the way that chemical and physical energies are localized, and that it has a limited energy value and radius of action. By transplantation it is possible to produce meaningless misconstructions which make it appear that no will for wholeness is at work here and that a mechanical process is quite simply unfolding.

Whence comes it that nature gives this bifurcated answer to man's question? It cannot happen because nature in itself is bifurcated. The ground of it must rather be that the question with which we approach nature is wrongly formulated. Where then does the error lie in our human question? Clearly it is erroneous for us to posit an opposition between a living cell and a machine, and then to ask whether a living cell is like a machine, or whether it obeys some other law. For a machine, say a watch or a musical box which is driven by a spring and plays a tune, is always a macroscopic structure. The metal parts of which, in large measure, it is composed, are rigid bodies. But these 'rigid bodies' are not rigid structures at all in the light of our present knowledge about the essence of matter. They are composed of masses of fundamental particles which are involved in a most rapid internal motion. If, therefore, we look round the inorganic world in order to find a structure with which to compare the organic structure of a living cell, and thus to demonstrate the difference between two natural realms, we ought not to take a highly developed macro-physical structure like a machine, but rather ought we to pay attention here also to an elementary structure. We must therefore compare a small single-celled entity, such as a virus, with an elementary structure of the inorganic world, say a molecule or an atom. If these elementary structures are there in both terms of the comparison, it appears, as we have already seen, that there is a striking similarity between the fundamental components of the organic and the inorganic worlds. An inorganic fundamental particle, as for instance a basic element of crystalline stuff, shows a tendency to construct the wholeness of its form by assimilation from its environment, to resist attack, and to multiply itself.

It may be objected that even if elementary structures in the inorganic world should have organic properties, the fact remains that a compound inorganic structure, like a machine, is governed by blind causality, which is not the case in the organic world, because there everything happens in a planned way. Is there not, therefore, an undeniable contrast between an organism and the causal-mechanism of a machine? To this we must reply that this impression arises because we fall at this point into the same error to which we have already alluded. We compare a simple structure of the organic world, a single-celled entity, with a complex structure of the inorganic world, namely a machine. If we are to avoid this error, we must take from the organic world not simple entities but complex entities, and compare a complex organic structure with the complex inorganic structure of the machine. The moment we do this, a striking similarity between the two at once appears. Within the realm of human life we may consider the total effect of statistically established facts relating to cities of more than a million population, statistics, say, of the annual number of cases of breaking and entering, or of suicide, or of preventible railway accidents. The numbers provided are relatively constant. The variations in these numbers are attributable to a ' blind causality '. The increase and decrease in the weekly suicide rate is conditioned by the time of year and other such factors. The annual number of injuries from railway accidents can be calculated and incorporated into the budgets of insurance companies with almost the same certainty as eclipses of the sun or the moon. And yet every single instance is explicitly a decision taken by a responsible person. If this is the case in human life, when we look at mass-tendencies, how much more must the total effect of an enormous number of single decisions give the impression of calculable causal happening when it is not human decisions that we are observing, but rather movements within the unimaginably greater multitudes of micro-organisms such as cholera bacilli or streptococci! Their behaviour can be predicted just as exactly as can the chemical reactions of matter or the behaviour of gas molecules at a given pressure and temperature. For in both cases we are not dealing with the elementary units but with mass formations as such. And now let us be quite clear on the point that the 'blind causality' by which a clock works when it is wound up, the certainty with which its behaviour may be predicted, are conditional on the fact that the stable parts of the mechanism (its wheels, weights, etc.) will remain constant and not alter their form or their mass. This constancy of machine parts, however, is shown by modern atomic theory to be itself a mass-effect which comes about because an average effect arises out of the movements of trillions of elementary entities which whirr round one another in a given raindrop or steel shaving, and its average value is constant. Is it not the case that human armies, running nowadays to a million or more men, can have the effect of a machine, an instrument in the hand of a great general, the movements of which can be causally predicted and taken into account as clear factors in a plan of battle? And yet the tremendous blows which a general is capable of delivering by means of this machine are composed of the single decisions and personal efforts of responsible men. If now we think of the largest army which has ever been employed as a whole in modern warfare, and multiply it by a million so that its smallest combat unit will consist of billions of soldiers, it will surely be the case that any slight differences between the decisions taken by various separate soldiers will be entirely irrelevant, whereas their effect may be noticeable in an army even of a million men. In an army of a million million, there will be a statistical average effect in any united operation which, for purposes of calculation, can be taken as an absolutely constant factor. Such an army, in the hand of a super-general, would be a machine working with absolute precision. The relationship in which such a general would stand to his army is precisely the same as that in which the engineer or qualified technician stands to his machine which may be a loom or a blast furnace or a steam hammer. Such a workman in fact resembles a strategist who is able to set in motion vast armies by simply pressing a button or pulling a lever. His 'armies' are the hordes of fundamental particles, which will produce a calculated mechanical effect because they remain 'in formation'. From an aeroplane which is so high above a parade ground that individual men cannot be distinguished, companies of marching soldiers will look like grey rigid bodies which, without losing their shape, are being drawn in a particular direction by a magnet. When we look at the parts of a machine with the naked eye, we are all in the position of the airman looking down from such a height on a parade ground. We are not able to make out the single structures out of which wheels and gears and shafts are composed. We see only compact masses, and from a distance these behave like rigid bodies moving with implacable necessity. The impression of rigidity arises merely from the human point of view. But the standards by which we study reality from our human standpoint are only relative. If it were possible for us to get away from our human perspectives and look at the world from the point of view of an entity millions of times smaller than ourselves, say a virus, then each of the molecules of which a machine part is composed would seem as big as ourselves, and the compact masses of rigid bodies would dissolve before our eyes into moving elements swarming round each other like bees. The machine therefore gives this impression of a dead mechanism because we are able to see its component parts only as mass structures within our human system of reference. If we were able to dissect them into their elementary parts, we should have before our eyes the same mystery that is found in living cells, though in a different form and at another level.

If this is true, we can no longer put the question, at any rate in its customary sense, as to how it came about that life appeared on the rigid crust of the earth quite suddenly at a certain stage in its process of cooling. This question always takes it for granted that when individual structures appeared, characterized by wholeness, nourishing themselves and propagating themselves, something wholly new was introduced; the 'wonder of life' dropped suddenly from heaven on to the dead, cold surface of the earth, and covered it with a plenitude of creaturely beings. But now it has been shown that this 'wonder' of self-nourishing, self-propagating wholeness does not come first into the picture with the arrival of organic life. It was there already from the beginning, with the creation of matter. In organic life-cells it has simply assumed a more highly developed form. A living cell is no more wonderful in itself than is a molecule, or one of the elementary structures whose multiplication produces a crystalline substance, the carbon atom in a diamond for instance. If we allow that a new world epoch began with the appearance of organic life on our planet, we can just as well see a turning point in world history when the first crystal was formed, and we can ask with equal justification how such a marvellous structure could arise with its inexhaustible power of constantly renewing its perfect form out of the resources of its environment. Did it come here by means of a meteor falling from the depths of space, i.e. by 'planetary inoculation', or did it occur by spontaneous generation, *generatio aequivoca*?

What attitude does all this suggest that we should take up in regard to the old argument as to whether the mechanistic or the vitalistic interpretation of life is correct? In the first place, the mechanical theory of life loses its point if by mechanicalism we understand the attitude which treats life cells as comparable with machines. For the machine which is brought in to explain the life cells has itself dissolved into living units which present us with the same question as does the process of life which we are seeking to explain by reference to it. On the other hand, however, we cannot come down quite simply on the side of vitalism, for this attitude assumes that with the origin of organic life a new natural factor comes into play which simply did not exist before the emergence of life and is not to be found outside the organic world. But it has been shown that everywhere, outside organic life, we are confronted with mysterious wholenesses which construct themselves on principles akin to those of life. If we want to express in a single phrase the attitude to which we have been brought, we may call it a total neo-vitalism. For we must drop the barriers which H. Driesch wanted to erect by using his entelechy-concept between life and 'dead' matter. We must extend to all fundamental structures the conclusions which Driesch reached by his experiments with simple organisms, modified as they have been by the tests of

Spemann and his school, and we must erect them into a world-principle whereby the whole objective world is constructed in a hierarchy of more highly developed forms. However deeply we may penetrate into the interior of organic and inorganic structures with the aid of the electronic microscope, we shall never come upon a homogeneous mass which was once taken to be the ultimate fabric of reality. The more deeply we penetrate, the more this fundamental stuff is seen to resolve itself into a 'hierarchy' of wholenesses, conflicting with one another, and then including and embracing one another. An atom of hydrogen with its positively charged nucleus round which there circles a negatively charged electron, or an atom of helium with its two circling electrons each in a quantum track which seems to have been carved out for it, is such a wholeness, a system moved through itself and held together by electrical equivalence, which already confronts us with all the wonder of creation. We can destroy this wholeness by bombardment, but we cannot restore it. We cannot understand how it in fact originated. We can only accept it as a given wholeness, observe it spectroscopically and describe it mathematically. The same is true of the atom complexes, or molecules, from which, according to structural chemistry, any stuff is made. We can only establish by actual tests whether, for instance, the molecules in any one of the ninety-eight elements known to us are so constructed that their atoms will combine with one hydrogen atom or whether two are necessary in order to produce, not merely a mixture, but a union which yields something new. Granted this knowledge about powers of combination (or 'valencies'), the chemical industry can proceed with its syntheses. We do not understand why, in crystalline substances like cooking salt, the molecules or atoms arrange themselves in regular patterns and make lattices in space, so that when light waves fall upon them they produce the phenomenon of refraction. We can only establish these facts experimentally, and then say that this is because of the mysterious structural law according to which the wholeness-structure of the molecule in question is built. The molecule behaves on a lower level just as the living cell behaves on a higher level, assimilating certain material from its environment and rejecting other material.

Here, therefore, we have discovered a fundamental law which holds throughout reality with ever-changing variations, which we must accept as a fundamental datum. A provisional formulation of this wholeness-law or form-principle would be as follows: In every fundamental structure, everything possible happens in order to build up the form appropriate to the structure in question, to maintain it and to diversify it at a higher level. This principle of wholeness must occupy the same place in the new organic picture of nature as did the fundamental relationships of pressure, impulse and gravitation exerted on rigid bodies in the old mechanistic picture. In the age of mechanism, these were the three fundamental processes to which it was hoped to trace back all natural events, and they were accepted as fundamental data which required no further explanation and behind which it was futile to probe. At this fundamental place we must now, in the new organic world-picture, put the *wholeness-tendency*.[1] It is the basic process to which all other events must be traced back, and which itself cannot be traced back to anything more fundamental. Natural explanation henceforth must mean recognizing in all natural phenomena the power of this form-building law, operating in new variations and combinations, whether the phenomena be those of the motion of electrons or the behaviour of giant molecules or living cells or the more highly developed organisms which are fashioned out of these cells. This basic principle is a fundamental datum as incapable of further explanation as were the effects of pressure and impulse on rigid bodies in the old mechanical form of natural explanation. The fact that in each elementary structure everything that can happen does happen so as to build up the appropriate form, to maintain it and to diversify it on a higher level, is no more wonderful and mysterious than that large rigid bodies do not pass through one another but set one another in motion by pressures and impulses. It is only the force of custom which makes the rolling of a sphere down an inclined plane or the fall of a

[1] *Ganzheitstendenz.*

stone which has been thrown into the air seem more intelligible to optically conditioned men like ourselves than is the invisible power by which a cell seeks to reconstitute its form whenever it has been damaged.

Once we have made the transition from mechanistic to organic thinking, and have built up our whole picture of nature on this new foundation, we become aware of having reached the limit of our objective natural knowledge. We cannot go beyond the organic law of form construction with any natural explanations. All that we can do is to think our way more deeply into the essence of this principle, to probe more deeply by observation and reflection directed upon life processes into the mystery of the organic striving for wholeness which pervades all world events, and by testing different kinds of organism to illuminate from various sides the peculiar nature of this wholeness-tendency. But we can give no further explanation of this tendency; that is to say, we cannot trace it back to anything else.

Biologists are attempting today, by a continual set of experiments, to probe more deeply the laws according to which the wholeness-tendency operates in elementary organisms. The transplantation tests made by Spemann and his school, which we have referred to earlier, are particularly important for the light they throw on these laws. When the first results of these tests were published, it seemed at first as though the brave forward march of neo-vitalism had been halted and that a retreat was being sounded, the object being to return to the causal-mechanical explanation of life. For it seemed to have been proved that the restitution of which certain organisms are capable after having been damaged does not, as Driesch claimed for his classical instances, always take place with the intention of reconstructing the original form of the organism; rather is it possible to set the organism in a context where it produces utterly ridiculous and purposeless misconstructions. But what obstructs the development of the wholeness-tendency in these latest experiments is not dead stuff but something which itself is organic. For the restrictions by which an organism can be induced to produce developments not in accord with its inner structure may have one of two grounds.

Either they occur because there is present not merely *one* wholeness, constructing and multiplying itself from the material in the environment, but *several* organic structures fighting over the same material. Or they occur because the wholeness-tendency of a living entity has suffered artificial interference from human beings who have transferred the entity to a new context where it develops in contradiction to itself.

Let us look at the first of these cases. When the abdominal skin of a salamander, grafted on to a frog's head, produces adhesive organs which, however, are not those of a frog but those of a salamander, the whole process can only be explained by the wholeness-tendency. It is an instance of the wholeness-tendencies of two different organisms fighting over the same building material and producing in the end a futile compromise. The situation is more complicated in the second case where it is not a matter of conflict between two wholeness-tendencies in different organisms, but rather of the form-building principle of a living entity being reduced to self-contradiction. This happens, not by the grafting of one organism on to another, but when a group of cells within one organism is transferred to another part of it; when, for instance, a group of cells is transplanted at a sufficiently early plastic stage to a point where it can be influenced by its new environment to produce a leg, whereas at a later stage it cannot be deflected from its original determination and produces a tail even though a tail at that point is quite absurd. The wholeness-tendency in this case also must be taken as self-explanatory. Apart from it there would be no possible explanation of why, at the point in question, a salamander's leg or a salamander's tail has appeared. But because of the dominating act of grafting by the experimenter, a situation has arisen which can be illustrated from human relationships in this kind of way.

A company of engineers is given the task, by the higher command, of building a bridge across a river at a particular point, in order to allow the infantry to cross. Because of a mistake in the transport command, they are taken to a point lower down the river where no bridge is necessary because the infantry are already across in that sector. At this point, however, there is a railway track which has been damaged by the enemy and that ought to be repaired. The local commander gives the order for this repair to be done. Two things can happen. This order might reach the company in time, in which case they deal with the new situation. Or the order might arrive too late, and the company feels bound by blind military discipline to do the job they were originally told to do, and therefore begins to build a bridge even though there is no point in doing so. The interference of a human transplanter in the development of a growing organism may well produce in similar fashion a pointless construction. But what is at work here is not a blind causal mechanism. We should rather compare it with the blind military discipline by which the company does the original job at the wrong place where it is quite unnecessary. The case is similar when the process of regeneration induced by interference from outside and abnormal treatment of the wounds produces purposeless misconstructions, say a double head on a snake, or several lenses in one eye, which tend to inhibit one another. But such products of a misdirected process of regeneration are not futile lumps of flesh or tissue. Seen in themselves, they are organic structures whose form has sprung from the wholeness-idea of an organism, and which, in their proper context, are able to fulfil a necessary function. As they are, however, they are parts of a cosmic body which have been detached from their original context and crop up with the purposeless wandering of meteors in space.

The principle of wholeness is not brought into question by the other fact which Spemann has established, namely that the power which determines the cells in favour of the construction of a particular form spreads out in concentric waves from an organizing centre, the *Urmund,* and that therefore wholly determinate material, the 'organizers', is available from this centre. It merely illustrates the method by which this mysterious factor permeates a medium in which it has to work and exercise its organizing influence. The comparison of this dissemination of organizing power with the simple wave motion which occurs in a pond when a stone is thrown into it is not a true one. For what is spreading here is not simply the mutual impact of parts of a material medium, as when a stone rolling down a steep slope hits another stone, and both go on to dislodge still others. It is a form-building power which is radiating in the organism, by which the cells in the neighbourhood, which in themselves are capable of producing anything, are induced to construct a highly complicated form such as the lens in an eye. If a comparison is wanted, it is much better to think of the influence which goes out into political life from an organizing centre like Moscow, and spreads a particular form of human social life through a whole country. We see, therefore, that even the purposeless structures which may arise under certain conditions are not the effects of blind causality. Rather do they arise out of a conflict between the wholeness-tendencies of different organisms, or because of the artificial interference of an experimenter in the growth of organisms. The transplantation tests, and the discovery of an organizing centre and of organizers, are not arguments against the validity of the wholeness-law but are new confirmations of it. They take us back along new routes to the mysterious fundamental law which governs the whole process of nature, and is repeatedly exemplified in new variations from the case of the simplest atom to that of the most highly developed organism.

When this fundamental law comes into sight, we stand at the boundary of all objective explanation of nature. There is no higher law to which we can trace it back or from which we can infer it or give it a basis. There is only one way by which to come one step nearer to an understanding of this fundamental law. This is revealed when we go behind the whole space of the objective world which limits the investigations of natural science and get back to the *non-objective* space to which we ourselves belong as non-perceptible subjects. The place at which I myself stand is the only point from which a direct glimpse is afforded to me of the interior of a wholeness event. I am aware that I am able to give orders which proceed from my brain through the channels of the motor nerves to my limbs, that these orders follow a particular plan and co-operate in a purposeful manner to nourish my body, defend it from danger, and propagate my like. This planned direction of our members, which we achieve every day on countless occasions, is in fact the only analogy which we can use to help us understand the organic wholeness-tendency from within. Even Driesch, in his *Philosophy of the Organic,* continually illustrates the restitutions which we observe in damaged organisms by reference to the planned measures which are taken by a man when a work on which he is engaged suffers damage. We are reminded involuntarily of the planned behaviour of a thinking man when we see how a primitive organism which has been damaged chooses between two different methods which are open to it in order to reconstitute its form. If the gills of a clavellina are cut away, it may very well produce another head from the stump in three or four days, as does an earthworm. But in about half of the observed cases, something quite different and much more rare takes place. It is not the lower part, the remaining stump, but the severed gills, which takes over the new construction. First the severed part reabsorbs all its organs, and transforms itself into a white ball with a very simple interior construction. It remains for two to three weeks in this state of creative repose. Then it begins to writhe and stretch until it transforms itself into a new, very small, but complete clavellina. We are reminded of a sculptor modelling a statue out of clay, who accidentally breaks off an important piece of the model and so has to think again about how to do his job. Either he chooses to go on working with the remaining part, or he pounds the material together again into a lump and begins from the beginning to create his statue afresh on a smaller scale. A similar impression is given when we take a *Tubularia* whose hydrant has been cut off but which has started on its process of restitution, and damage it again in order to see which way it will choose to reach its goal in spite of the new damage. When, for instance, the *Tubularia* has reached the stage of producing its two new sets of tentacles in the form of red rings, the upper ring may be cut off and the whole restitution sabotaged. What happens? There are three possibilities available. The organism may divide the remaining strip into two by producing a band in the middle. Or it may complete the remaining crown of tentacles, thrust it forth, and supply the missing funnel by sprouting from surface tissues. Or, finally, it may retract everything that has so far been produced in the way of restitution, begin the work all over again, and construct everything afresh to meet the new conditions. 'Thus there is in fact a kind of equi-finality of restitution; a point of departure, a goal, and three different means and methods' between which a decision has to be made. Driesch compares the decision to that of a human draughtsman who, in the course of his drawing, discovers that he will not be able to get all his design on to the paper. 'What is he to do? Either he can scrap what he has done, choose a new piece of paper with greater care, and use it for the remainder of his work; or he can rub out the old drawing and begin a new one on a smaller scale; or, finally, he can produce a compromise and complete the sketch by rubbing out a few lines here and there and re-drawing them, and the rest of the pattern, so as to get it all on to the paper at the cost of distorting the proportions of his subject here and there.'

Spemann, too, compares the transformation of the salamander's skin when grafted on to the head of a frog to an order which is sent out from the headquarters of the new locality to the point of grafting: 'Adhesive organs of the mouth!' The transplanted cells receive the order just as would a detachment of soldiers transferred from one army into another where their own language is not spoken. They translate it literally into their own language and produce the adhesive organs, not of a frog but of a salamander.

In all such cases we are tempted to suppose that a thinking mind inhabits these primitive organisms and that whenever a calamity occurs it takes over and calculates how the damage is to be repaired with the least effort and building material. It is not without justification that we make use of the analogy of the superior human understanding to shed light on the processes of regeneration. For this is the only analogy available to us. But this analogy does not take us the whole way in helping us to understand. For this organic form-building power of simple organisms achieves bigger results than men achieve with their understanding and their technical and constructional equipment. The so-called clairvoyant instinct possessed by many simple organisms produces effects which the human intellect can only achieve on a basis of tedious observations and calculations, and does it with a certainty which we can never reach. A few acknowledged facts will serve to illustrate this. The various kinds of paralysing hymenoptera (wasps) perform a skilful surgical operation on the spiders, beetles or grubs in which they lay their eggs, which has the effect of paralysing without killing these creatures which their larvae then use as fresh food. 'The wasp which uses the larva of the Rose-chafer stings it at one particular point, but it is a point where the motor ganglion-cells are concentrated to the exclusion of anything else. . . . The species of digger wasp which uses the cricket knows that it has three nerve centres which govern the motion of its three pairs of legs; or at any rate it behaves as though it knew this. It stings the insect first in the neck, then at the front of the thorax, and finally at the beginning of the abdomen. . . . The hairy ammophila stings the grub which it uses in nine different nerve centres and then attacks its head, biting into it just so far as to produce paralysis without death.' Men could only perform operations of this kind after the most careful study of anatomy and the nervous system, and then only by surgical training and the use of the most delicate instruments. The wasps do it without any education or previous preparation. There is a black weevil,[1] three or four millimetres long, which makes an S-shaped cut in a birch leaf, and then with its legs it rolls the leaf (the upper side outwards) into a tight tube which is shaped like an ice-cream cornet. Before it does the rolling it carves out one or two tiny pockets at the base of the leaf as cradles for its eggs and larvae. When the larvae hatch out, they feed on the leaf. Heinrich Prell now dissents from the earlier theory of the mathematician Heis that the S-curve is related to the edge of the leaf as an evolute to one of its involutes and that therefore the beetle has solved the most difficult mathematical problem of constructing the evolute from the involute. But Prell concludes,

---

[1] *Deporaus (Rhyncites) betulae.*

nevertheless, that 'it is utterly unthinkable that such a complicated process as the rolling of the funnel could take place step by step. A slight error at any point would make the whole thing impossible. We are therefore driven to the assumption that such a complex biological operation takes place, so to speak, at one blow.'

But the practical ability of the organic wholeness-tendency exceeds that of technical human intelligence not merely in that it can achieve directly and with astonishing sureness things which men could only do in a circuitous fashion with the aid of observations and calculations. What is even more astounding and beyond our human understanding is the way in which animal instinct seems to penetrate with clairvoyant pre-vision into the future, when we consider the provision it makes for the coming generation. The horse-fly lays its eggs at a particular point on the horse's shoulder or leg. It behaves as though it could foresee the following events which take place one after another: when the eggs are hatching, the horse will lick them off with its tongue; thus they will pass into the alimentary canal and so into its stomach. There the larvae will find all the conditions necessary for their growth. A still more remarkable instance is that of the sitaris beetle, which lays its eggs at the entrance of a subterranean passage made by a certain kind of bee (*Anthophora*). Why does it choose that precise point? Because the following events are 'clairvoyantly pre-visaged': the sitaris larvae wait at the entrance to the passage until the male bee crawls out to make its nuptial flight. It climbs on to the bee's back and clings there during the flight of the bee. When, high in the air, the male bee has intercourse with the female bee, the larvae take this opportunity of changing planes in mid-air and move over to the female bee. When the female returns to the nest where she has built up her store of honey, she begins, after a time, to lay her eggs, and the sitaris larva fastens upon an egg and destroys its interior in a few days. Then it uses the shell as a support and a raft so as not to sink into the honey, and floats on the surface of the honey, feeding on it until it is strong enough to develop into a fully fledged insect.

Now if we men wanted to carry out a plan like that, in the

interest, say, of a carefully planned burglary, we could only do it after careful study of the habits, marriage customs and domestic arrangements of the bee in question, and after a careful calculation of the risks entailed. But this little beetle can take no such steps, for two entities are involved in the carrying out of the plan and they can never come to any arrangement about it. There is the beetle which lays its eggs at this peculiarly suitable place, and there is the larva which emerges from the egg and carries out its part of the plan without any parental instruction but with a clairvoyant certainty. And each action involved makes sense only on the assumption that all the rest will be successfully performed and the ultimate goal will be reached.

From these facts we see that the process which alone is really familiar in our human experience, the process of technical behaviour based on observation and calculation, does not go far enough to help us understand the practical achievements of the organic form-building tendency in primitive organisms. We know only one way to create a planned whole: we must have a goal in view; then, by a study of the laws which govern the course of nature, we must determine what possibilities are open to us in order to reach this goal; from this emerges the plan we must carry out in order to reach the goal as quickly as possible. Only when these three conditions are fulfilled does a structural wholeness emerge at our hands which gives evidence of a unified plan and of direction from a single centre. But this planning and technical construction of which we are capable is manifestly only one of the ways by which the wholeness-tendency can operate in producing and preserving a structure. There are other ways alongside it, though they are not open to our direct understanding. We can see objectively, from outside, how these other ways inherent in nature work out in practice. But we do not see the inner side of the process which happens before our eyes. It may be that we have some kind of feeling for this instinctive behaviour of animals and plants if there is still alive in us a trace of the magical relationship to nature which men once enjoyed. For the ritual of magic served, as we saw earlier, to put primitive man's existence into direct relationship with the powers which rule within nature. He did not interfere technically, from outside, in the course of nature. He moved the natural powers magically from within so as to bring them into the service of his own preservation. But of course we cannot say with certainty whether what lies behind the instinctive behaviour of animals is like what lies behind the magical rites of primitive man, or whether it is something quite different to which we have no access whatever. The word 'instinct' is only a symbol of our ignorance. We use it just as the symbol x is used in algebra. We mean by it an unknown magnitude to which we can assign no definite value. But in any case, we are reminded by this instinctive behaviour, just as we are reminded by the effects produced in magic, that there are ways other than the planned conduct of technical man by which to achieve the construction and the preservation of an organic wholeness. For all these ways are only special cases of the one fundamental law which governs all wholeness-structures; they are all effects of the wholeness-tendency which we cannot explain further, but can only describe. If we were able to review the varying forms and modes in which this fundamental law expresses itself within the whole of reality, we should feel much as we do when we think of the many varieties of electro-magnetic waves which differ only in frequency. The spectrum which alone is visible to us, with its range of light from red to violet, includes only such waves as have a frequency between four and eight hundred billions per second. That is a single octave. But we know that above and below this visible octave there are other invisible electro-magnetic waves whose presence can be detected by their effects. By their heat effect we can tell, in this indirect way, that there are eight or so infra-red octaves, and by their chemical effects we know that there are five ultra-violet octaves. X-rays, for instance, lie beyond the violet, and beyond the red are the wireless waves used in radio telephony. Though, therefore, we are able to see directly only a single octave in this tremendous multiplicity of waves and must deduce the rest from their effects, and although even these visible waves are vastly different from one another, all such waves belong essentially together in a single unity. They are all electro-magnetic waves.   So with our present concern. We may start our review of the many different effects of the wholeness-tendency from the special case which alone is known to us directly from inside, and then draw conclusions about other cases by the principle of continuity, although we only know of the presence of these other cases indirectly, by means of their objective effects.

25. THE NON-OBJECTIVE POINT OF REFERENCE OF THE LIFE-PROCESS

This brings us within sight of a conclusion which has far-reaching significance for our world-view.   It is not a conclusion marked by the certainty of an observation or of an experimentally established fact.   For here we have to reach behind everything that can be observed objectively.   Nevertheless this conclusion is one to which we are inexorably driven by the principle of continuity.   It is this: We know that behind the one 'octave' which is directly accessible to us within the vast range of possibilities for 'wholeness-effects' there stands an 'I', the imperceptible entity which we can only refer to by the first person singular, but which is there behind our own planned conduct.   This planned conduct by which, on the basis of long experience, I promote the welfare of my body and defend it from external attack is scarcely conceivable apart from a non-objective point of reference. When I seek shelter underground in an air-raid, or when I secure a job at which to earn my living, or whatever similar goal I attain in the interest of self-preservation by co-ordinating the operation of my members and sense-organs according to plan, there is a hidden director behind such action which acts, on the one hand, as a knowing I, receiving the impressions which inform me about my situation and the available opportunities, and on the other hand, in the rôle of a willing I, gives to my physical organs the orders which they are to carry out if the goal is to be reached as quickly as possible.   The fact that I react in this planned way to impressions from the external world in order to preserve my body is closely related, as we saw earlier, to my being irrevocably and immutably committed to this body, which I refer to as my own body. I can contemplate the fate of other bodies with the detached interest of an observer, unless indeed I participate in that fate by virtue of some deep-lying connection. But whether I wish to do so or not, I have to devote all my powers to the preservation of the one body which has been committed to my responsibility. However passive a disposition a man may have, all his powers are called into play when his own body is threatened by death. This body is the position I have to hold and defend under all circumstances and to the very limit of my resources, against the powers which threaten my life. We must therefore conclude, in accordance with the principle of continuity, that there must be a non-objective reference point for self-defence and self-regulation which we observe in wholeness, though in a different form from anything which is available in human experience. Further, the energy with which these quite different structures reconstruct and reconstitute themselves in face of all external shocks must depend on the fact that their existence has an inner side which bears some analogy, however remote, to our human inner life. They also must stand in relation to an entity which controls their destiny and does not belong to perceptible space.

In all this there still persists, quite naturally, the unbridgeable gulf between an atom in the sense of the Bohr model and a living cell; the opposition to which A. Wenzl draws attention in his essays on the organic world-picture when he says: 'The wholeness-character of the Bohr-Pauli atom is a mathematically static or stationary one, whereas that of the organism is genetically dynamic. The organism, as Driesch puts it, is an organism in process of becoming; we must leave open the question of how the atom comes to be.' But, particularly since the discovery of radio-activity and nuclear fission, we know that more happens in the atom than transferences and changes of state in the electron shell, which is what you get in the case of chemical reactions. There are also elemental transformations which alter the inner structure of the nucleus. The collapse of a radium atom is an instance of nuclear transformation which is continually taking place. It is from this collapse that the radiation emanating from radium proceeds. Even atoms, therefore, can die a natural death, or in some cases a violent one. If they can die, they must also have been born. They have an average life-span, even though it is one which embraces dimensions of time unattainable by living cells. When Madame Curie, the discoverer of radio-activity, noticed these explosions within the atomic world, she was at once reminded of the fate of living entities. 'In what appears to be lifeless material,' she wrote, 'there are births, collapses, deaths and suicides. They conceal dramas which unfold with ineluctable necessity. They conceal life and death.' As we have already pointed out, the fact that no abso-lute distinction separates the world of atoms from the world of living cells becomes more clearly apparent when we do not compare the atom with the living cell, but rather compare with the cell the atom complex or union which we call a molecule. As we move down the ladder of living structures from many-celled entities to simpler ones, we come first to the bacteria and then to even smaller structures, the bacterio-phagus and the virus. We come therefore into close proximity to the molecule. The tobacco mosaic virus seems to Pascual Jordan to be a single molecule, though one of tremendously high molecular weight (in the region of twenty-five million). It contains hundreds of thousands of carbon, nitrogen and other atoms. At a further stage we find in the nucleus of the embryo cell, or more exactly in its chromosomes, the 'genes' which carry the various inherited properties. The gene, this unit of heredity, is similar to an individual virus in being a single large molecule containing between a thousand and a hundred thousand atoms. Therefore the distinction between a highly complex wholeness-structure, a giant molecule and a living cell, is clearly a gradual one and no longer one of abso-lute opposition. Our present research techniques have not yet afforded to us a glimpse into the inner working of a giant molecule, but once we succeed, possibly with the aid of the electron microscope, in obtaining a perceptible picture of the processes which occur within this small but inexhaustible world of the giant molecule, it will still be possible to say *a priori* that, however far we go in illuminating the inner world of a molecule and whatever sights are unveiled before our eyes, there can never be anything other than the harmonious co-operation of movement between component elements constructing and constantly renewing a particular kind of wholeness. The picture of the inner processes taking place in the deep interior of the organism which deeper and more penetrating observation will doubtless provide, will be one of processes which we see only from outside and whose invisible background remains for ever concealed from us. Even with closer observation we shall be, in respect of such a life-process, in the situation of a deaf man in a concert hall. He sees the movements of the violinists and the horn players which accompany the production of the piece of music. He sees how their arms and hands respond to the movements of the conductor's baton. But he cannot see into the deeper ground of these harmonious movements. For this is imperceptible to him by reason of his nature. It can only be grasped by one whose ear is open to the meaning of the music. Our case would be similar even if we were able to probe more deeply than is possible today into the interplay of the elements within the interior of a giant molecule which governs an organism's process of becoming. The point of control from which the orchestra of atomic processes is conducted is just as imperceptible as is the will which lies behind the interplay of movement among a man's organs when he does his morning exercises or when he makes a speech for the defence in a law court and accompanies it with appropriate gestures.

It is only objectively and from outside that we are able to see the physical and biological processes which take place even in a highly complex molecule. We can only offer opinions about the inward picture. But if, in accordance with the principle of continuity, we may take it that infra-red and ultra-violet rays have the same structure as have rays in the octave from red to violet which can be seen by human eyes, then, by the law of continuity, we must suggest that wholeness-structures which are entirely different and essentially simpler in construction than the human or animal organism will have a fundamental structure similar to that of highly developed entities. We must assume that these simpler wholeness-systems also have a non-objective inner side, and that in their case also the direction of the whole has a point of reference which lies in non-objective space and stands in similar relation to the structure which is in the objective world as does the non-perceptible self in our case to the body which each of us calls his own.

The factor which regulates the mutual action as a whole of the parts of an organism Driesch calls an 'intensive manifold', in contrast with the 'extensive manifold' which it serves to direct. How is this to be understood? An extensive manifold, according to his definition, is a 'manifold of a typical kind, whose separate elements are spatially next to one another, or temporarily after one another, or both, but always in a typical order'. The interplay of processes which go to construct an organism or to reconstitute it after damage, is therefore, seen from outside, an extensive manifold. 'The ground of origin of extensive manifolds thus defined, whether they be organisms or machines, cannot, however, in its turn, be an extensive manifold of the machine type. . . . The genuine organism as presented to observation is certainly a combination of separate parts, each of which can be described in physical or chemical terms, as with a machine. . . . But the ultimate ground of the combination, and of all its changes, is not itself an agent, or a combination of agents, such as we are familiar with in physics and chemistry. It rests on entelechy. . . . We will call all kinds of entelechies or psychoids "intensive manifolds", certainly they contain something of the nature of a "manifold", but the elements of this manifold are neither spatially next to one another nor temporarily after one another. We may say that entelechy is manifold in conception but simple as a natural agent.' It is not possible to give an intelligible philosophical account of what Driesch means here by intensive manifold so long as we are working only with a Euclidean space in which objects always occur either next to one another or after one another. A manifold whose elements appear neither in spatial proximity nor in temporal succession and yet are not merged in undifferentiated unity can only be described philosophically if we make a distinction between the whole space of objectivity and a non-objective space where the content of the real world is disposed in an entirely different way from what we discover in perceptible space. It is only in non-perceptible space that we can have contents which are different from one another and yet lie in one another rather than being separated into spatial proximity and temporal succession. This, however, is the case with those elements which, according to Driesch, present an entelechy. It is in restitution processes that Driesch chiefly tries to exhibit the supra-spatial omnipresence of the entelechy, where organisms like the tubularia and clavellina reconstitute their form after being damaged. The cut which severs the head from the rump may be made at any point, and every time what ought to happen according to the building plan of the whole does in fact happen at the relevant point, so that from the available material the whole which expresses the omnipresent building plan may be reconstituted. The factor by which the construction is governed and the necessary measures adopted for the reconstruction of that particular form must therefore be equally present at every point within the entire organism. As we saw above, Spemann's evidence, that the form-building factor has an organizing centre where it is at its strongest and from which it disseminates its activity, is not a valid ground of objection to the supra-spatiality of the entelechy which Driesch assumes. For it is not a mechanical process, like the rolling of a ball which makes other balls roll by impact with them, which is disseminated from this basis of operations, but rather an event with wholeness, comparable to the carrying out of a plan, for the sake of which available cell groups are conscripted as material. This is only conceivable if motions are performed simultaneously at different points, as in the advance of an army, all of which lie within a unified plan of campaign. This requires a command post, with authority over the separate detachments and simultaneous contact with them all. Only under these conditions can each detachment be given the special task which is essential to the carrying through of the whole plan.

The fact that an entelechy transcends not merely spatial proximity but also temporal succession is particularly evident from biological data which led Richard Semon in his day, and nowadays have led his associate, E. Bleuler, to posit some form of memory. Why is it, asked Semon, that when a lizard grows a second tail after the loss of its first it has the simpler scaly structure which was fashionable among its cretaceous ancestors, the saurians? Something is at work here which, if a mental process were under discussion, we should call an act of memory. It is not, however, the 'memory' of a single individual. It is rather like the awakening of the childhood memories of a whole race, stimulated by some special occasion —in this case an injury, which drives the entire organism to re-enact a feature of that far-off time within the present environment. Semon assumed 'engrams' which have been impressed on the living substance in the course of its racial or generic development, as though it were a kind of wax tablet. He wanted to say that the totality of such 'engrams', received in the past or still being received, comprise the 'mneme'. This, of course, is not an explanation but simply an objective description or illustration of the mysterious fact which we are dealing with. For an 'engram' which persists like the impression of a seal on wax is a thing extended in space, a proximate entity, an extensive manifold. But the conformation of an organic structure, such as a lizard's tail, cannot be traced back to anything of that kind. What operates here can only be some kind of wholeness-tendency which produces a planned structure. If this particular inclination towards a form persists unaltered and unaffected by the generations of change which have taken place over thousands or hundreds of thousands of years and is still capable of developing its form-building power when the right opportunity comes, this must be because, as Driesch puts it, we have an intensive magnitude before us which does not merely transcend spatial proximities but also temporal proximities. We have therefore an imperceptible factor whose relationship to particular structures of the perceptible world is strictly comparable to the relationship of our human I to the human body.

That must suffice to round off our review of the present state of research into the mystery of life. What is the contribution which all this makes to the statement of the relationship between the process of nature and God? We discovered in the previous volume that we cannot achieve an encounter with God by objective contemplation of the great law-abiding complex of natural processes. It is only when we have encountered God in a wholly personal way that we first realize that it is no incomprehensible Fate but a living God who is behind all these ordinances. In accord with all that has been said so far, we can only come to this personal encounter with God when we follow the advice which Fichte gave to his pupils at the beginning of his theory of knowledge; that is to say, when we stop looking at all that surrounds us and concentrate solely on ourselves. As soon as I stop pushing myself out of the way and pause before my own existence, I find there are two puzzles which must be solved somehow or other if I am not to be misled. The first of these arises from the connection by which I am fettered in irrevocable and immutable fashion to the structure which I call my body; whether or not I prefer to do so, I must play out to the end the rôle which has been allotted to me in the great drama of human life in community. This puzzling connection involves for me an Either/Or. Either it is a frivolous chance which has washed me up at this precise point on the shore of the world, in which case my whole life is arbitrary and meaningless. Or I have been set at this point by an eternal Thou. In that case I am here under a divine commission. I can base my whole life on faith in the one who has put me here. The second riddle of my existence is my solitude. I can see directly only into myself. For all other entities I have no direct insight. I see only the objective external picture together with the effects and manifestations which proceed from it and I draw analogical conclusions with varying degrees of assurance about the invisible inner world which lies behind it. By being bound, once and for all, to this one body, I am irrevocably shut out from all others. The interior of these others remains hidden from me. I am like a prisoner sentenced for life to solitary confinement in a single cell within a vast prison of cells. I cannot look inside the cells occupied by other prisoners, and they can establish relations with me only indirectly and as need arises by knocking on the cell walls. The numerous tensions, misunderstandings, slanders, distortions and abuses which occur in human relationships arise for the most part because none of us can see into the other party and genuinely put himself into the other man's shoes. No one therefore can pass a really just and unprejudiced judgment on what is happening in the case of another man. This puzzle of solitude also cries out for some solution. And here too we stand before an Either/Or. Two possibilities are available. The first is that there is no way out from this solitude. Every separate being lives his solitary life isolated from all the others until he sinks into the Void. Each one, to the very last, is alone with himself and carries his secrets of life, whether happy or tragic, with him to the grave. The tensions, misunderstandings and slanders which arise between men remain for ever unclarified and unresolved. The only conclusion is that grass will grow over us all. Everything tends ultimately to go down into the eternal night and to sink beneath the waves of forgetfulness which sooner or later engulf all that man has thought or constructed or striven for. There is no point up above the flux to which man can appeal for a just judgment which resolves the tensions between man and man. This state of affairs is brought into question only by one hypothesis, namely that the second of the two possibilities is in fact the operative one. There is an omnipresent 'Thou'. It is, as Christ said, 'the Father who sees in secret', before whose eyes all the hidden background of existence stands exposed. All the cards we are playing are on the table before Him. All that goes on within us is open before Him like a book. He alone has no need to deduce from outward appearances, as we must, what moves us from within. This and this alone can mean the end of my solitude. For only in this case is there one to whose sight the prison walls which divide us from one another are transparent. He looks down from above into every cell simultaneously. He sees down to the roots of our being at every moment. If we should all be caught up in a welter of mutual misunderstanding because none can wholly think himself into another person's mind, there is one point at which we are all understood. We can put on an act in front of all our fellow men. But all the masks we wear for one another's benefit fall before Him. It is idle for us to seek to justify ourselves in His sight. We are all known, through and through, by Him from the start. 'There is no creature that is not manifest in his sight; but all things are naked and laid open before the eyes of him with whom we have to do' (Heb. 4.13). This one before whom we all stand is alone able to pass judgment rightly upon us and to be judge between us. He alone understands us with compassionate understanding, though all our fellow men condemn us. This being so, we can take up the same attitude to our life's work as that of Johann Sebastian Bach, to whom, particularly in his later life, it was a matter of indifference whether men understood his music provided that there was One to hear and to understand, One to whom he wished to offer all his works as a thank-offering upon an altar. Because our every thought is thought in His presence, we can genuinely talk over with Him everything that shocks us or moves us or refuses to be disposed of by our own ingenuity. This speech with Him, in which what lies within us is laid open like a book, is prayer. The strengthening which comes from prayer lies chiefly in the fact that here we are not talking to one whom we must first seek laboriously to know, but rather to one who knows us better than we know ourselves. This dialogue with the all-seeing all-knowing one who sees right through us is a genuine conversation with all misunderstanding ruled out from the start. It is the perfection of something which occurs only in an imperfect and preliminary form in our conversations with men. If the omnipresent God is real, then there is a community among men which is higher than all other communities which human life produces. It rests on the fact that all men stand before God. Therefore they are all brothers, even where they are cut off from one another by irreconcilable contradictions. By way of this community with God they also come into a unique kind of community among themselves.

These are the two riddles of our existence, both of which leave us confronting the ultimate Either/Or of that existence. In the first volume we were led to this existentialist position, but there it applied only to our human existence. Now, however, by this review of the present state of research into the mystery of life, it is not merely the whole world of life but also, beyond this, the entire world of wholeness-structures which comes within our scope. We are dealing with a manifold beyond human compass, an immeasurable fullness of different wholeness-systems from the inorganic molecule up to the most highly developed cellular entity. At first sight it seems as though the relationship we have to these subhuman wholenesses, such as animals, plants and inorganic entities whose silent enigmatic motions we observe, must be totally different from the relationship with our fellow men to whom we are able to speak. We cannot come to terms with non-human beings by the use of words. Any such being is therefore infinitely more foreign and far removed from us than is the most remote and enigmatic of our fellow men. We are able simply to draw necessary conclusions about what is going on within them from the movements carried out by these non-human entities. We can only experiment with them, as does for instance the zoologist when he seeks to establish the sense of colour and location in the bee. We can observe how they react to particular stimuli. But however great be the estrangement from which these non-human beings confront us, our relationship to them is fundamentally the same as to our fellow men. There is not a specific difference but only a gradual one. Our fellow men present to us only an outward picture. The inner picture is concealed. The cell wall of our 'I'-imprisonment prevents any direct glimpse into the interior. We are left to depend on unperceivable analogical conclusions. The difference is simply that in dealings with our fellow men there is much richer material available for drawing the conclusions than is the case with a sea-urchin or a comma-bacillus or a virus or an element in the composition of crystalline material. The deeper we descend into the inorganic realm the more difficult it is to find possibilities of comparison, and we grope in a fog. Only the continuity principle takes us from highly developed organisms down to the simpler formations. Everywhere we see wholenesses, and we must assume that they also stand in some kind of relation to the omnipresent imperceptible space.

Thus the Either/Or which holds at first only within our

human situation receives a far wider significance. This uncanny estrangement which we feel as characterizing the inner life of extra-human structures leaves us even more sharply face to face with the ultimate Either/Or than does our human relationship. When we think of the world which lies outside our human existence, the prison cells of which we spoke seem to extend to infinity. The men with whom we can come to terms by speech are like inhabitants of neighbouring cells, living next door to us on the other side of the cell wall so that they are able to give us clear, audible signs. But beyond these neighbouring cells there are more remote cells from which nothing penetrates to our solitude except muffled noises. When we watch a fly struggling to defend itself by feeble flutterings against a spider which has trapped it, or an injured worm twisting and turning without being able to make a sound, or when we see at sunset how the flowers fold their petals at the breath of an evening wind, or how they turn brown and die after a spring frost, we ask ourselves what is really happening within these creatures whose movements we are able to observe only from the outside; what kind of struggles and sufferings may be occurring inside them? But we can give no answer to this question. We exceed our competence if we give a negative answer to it and say that these can only be reflex motions behind which there lies at best an apathetic soul-life which cannot be compared at all to our human consciousness. This is to make the naïve human assumption that we men obviously enjoy the highest grade of soul-life, and that therefore inner life becomes more apathetic and worthless the less resemblance there is between its outward manifestation and that of human behaviour. All that we can say in fact, in every case, is this: we do not know what lies behind the sub-human entity by way of an inner world. What we say about it is like what a blind man says about colour.

In virtue of all this, the solitude which presses upon us even within our human context becomes something quite monstrous. An ocean of multifarious animate lives ebbs and flows around us on every side. But from the solitary rock on which we sit we can only see the surface of the waves. We suppose that in the unplumbed depths beneath this surface there lies a highly mysterious life, but it is hidden from our eyes. And this is the case not merely among ourselves but probably for all other creatures as well. Our inner destiny must be as strange and incomprehensible to them as theirs is to us. Therefore our relationship to the sub-human creatures also leaves us facing the ultimate Either/Or. Either, as Leibnitz said, the world is made up of solitary 'monads without windows' which remain for ever foreign to one another. Each monad goes its own solitary way, which is known to nothing save itself, until it reaches the end when it sinks into eternal night. Or there is an omnipresent being about whom we can not only say that the interior of no man is hidden from him, but also, in biblical words, that 'there is no *creature* that is not manifest in his sight; but all things are naked and laid open before the eyes of him with whom we have to do'. If this is the truth, and if we consciously acknowledge it, we shall have reached the feeling for nature and for the world enjoyed by the men who speak to us in the Bible. They were quite convinced that it was not manhood alone which had a direct relation with God but also the animal and plant worlds and even the inorganic world. First the world of animals: God is He 'who gives to the beast his food, to the young ravens which cry' (Ps. 147.9). Of the animals as such it is said: 'These all wait upon thee, that thou mayest give them their meat in due season' (Ps. 104.27). Not only animals, however, for the plants also have part in this joyful worship of God: 'all the trees of the field shall clap their hands' (Isa. 55.12); 'then shall all the trees of the wood rejoice before the Lord, for he cometh, he cometh to judge the earth' (Ps. 96.12f.). It is not only plants and animals which stand in worship of God. The inorganic world is included within this joyful congregation when God appears and reveals Himself: 'Let the heavens be glad and let the earth rejoice; let the sea roar, and the fullness thereof; let the field exult, and all that is therein' (Ps. 96.11ff.); 'Let the floods clap their hands; let the hills sing for joy together before the Lord, for he comes to judge the earth' (Ps. 98.8); 'Bless the Lord, all ye his works, in all places of his dominion' (Ps. 103.22). These are not merely pictorial

expressions or poetic turns of speech. For it is even clearer
in the New Testament than in the Old that the whole creation
is included, together with man, in a unity of life and community of destiny. The whole creation shares our longing for
liberation from its futile condition, to which it has been
reduced 'not of its own will'. It waits for the 'disclosure of
the sons of God' through whom 'the creation itself shall also
be delivered from the bondage of corruption into the liberty
of the glory of the children of God. For we know that the
whole creation groans and travails with us in pain until the
moment arrives' (Rom. 8.19ff.). We must come back, in a
later context, to the ultimate meaning of this biblical cos-
mology. But this much at least emerges from the passages
already quoted. According to the Bible, God is the eternal
point of reference at which the life-lines of all His creatures
intersect. Thus all the walls which create interior separation
between His creatures will be thrown down, and the solitude
which is there everywhere in the created world will be overcome.

We have now reached the end of this section in which we
have assembled the more important results of modern research
into the riddle of life. And we have come to the same conclusion as we reached about the other questions discussed
earlier. In each case we stand face to face with an absolute
according to which human research has been orientated and
which has come to acquire a certain religious value, for
example, matter, absolute space, absolute time and absolute
causal necessity. The mystery of life which we have been
investigating appears under the same aspect. Though it is
true that vitalism, in the first instance, is a purely biological
hypothesis, it also takes on the character of a religious value
when it passes over into the 'life-faith' which rose up in
opposition to Christian faith in the epoch of National Social-
ism. And here also we have seen the completion of the transformation which took place in respect of the other absolutes.
The collapse of vitalist living faith has not come about
through speculative means. It happened chiefly in consequence of deeper and more penetrating observation of the real
process of life. Animal life which is going on all around us

is not a peaceful idyll or paradise but a vast battlefield where war is being waged with deadly weapons. We see this in familiar things that happen every day, when a fly is caught in a spider's web and in spite of its feeble resistance is overwhelmed, trapped and finally eaten by its murderess, or when a woodpecker catches the grub for which it has spent its time tapping, drags it out of its hiding place and swallows it with complete callousness. Our attention has been drawn to yet more horrible forms of destruction, such as that practised by the paralysing wasps, whose formula for a particularly horrible kind of slaughter is to paralyse without killing by inflicting upon their victim at key points several paralysing stings whose ultimate effect is a slow and probably quite dreadful death. There is a further instance which we may use to illustrate the point that in the animal world the stronger forms of life prey upon the weaker quite mercilessly. A scientific worker told the story of his expedition into a side valley of the Amazon basin. He was in a lightly built canoe of the kind used by the natives. Suddenly, on the bank, he saw something which gripped his attention and which he will never be able to forget. A llama was quenching its thirst at the river's edge, and the explorer saw a leopard crouching in the bush above it ready to spring on the peaceful beast and tear it apart. The leopard sprang, and the two animals were locked in battle, when suddenly they fell apart and both let out a scream of terror. What had happened was that shoals of small fish which abound in those southern waters, their teeth sharp as razors, had suddenly come up from the depths of the river and fallen upon the two fighting animals to strip the flesh from them both. They finished their murderous work in a quarter of an hour. The terrible cries were silenced and the uncanny stillness of death lay over the dark water. The scientist was so shocked by the whole episode that he could not suppress the awful thought that if his canoe were to be smashed against a rock he too would share the fate of the two animals whose death struggles he had witnessed.

It is clear from this that the 'faith in life' to which at first sight the study of living creatures may bring us tends to collapse on closer examination, because, as Paul says in

Romans 1, the whole world of living things is shot through
with 'corruption', and, as he goes on to say in Romans, the
dreadful cry goes up from the suffering of corruptible
creatures for their deliverance from the bondage of corruption.

The two books by Friedrich Wilhelm Weber, *Der Altböse
Feind* (*The Ancient Enemy*) and *Gott in der Natur* (*God in
Nature*), contain such a wealth of pictures of horror that it
will be quite sufficient to select only a few in order to destroy
for ever all illusions about a peaceful animal world where
man is supposed to be the only disruptive influence. Weber
compares a flesh-eating plant with an inn which welcomes
its guests only to inflict upon them a horrible death. 'I am
shocked to the core when I think about the innocent visitor's
awful death which I see happening here. Each of the cellars
in the inn were fitted with pipes from which there flowed a
slimy sticky viscous fluid. Any guest who put a foot in this
morass could never get it out again. The more he struggled
in the slime and bog, the higher rose the morass. The point
came when he could hardly breathe. And then with my own
eyes I saw how the terrified unfortunate guest sank back into
this murderous swamp and gave up the struggle to live. Give
me air! I need it every time I think about this incident.
But my special task lies at this treacherous place. I must go
back to the Botanical Gardens and again go through the
experience I have described, first with the sarracenia and
again with the nepenthes. I grant you that my unfortunate
neighbour was a gnat. The spears which impaled it were set
at the base of the honey glands which barred the entrance
into the flower's interior. The slime was a glandular mucus
in the sac of the carnivorous plant. We know, indeed, that
certain insects can live in the death-cellar of the nepenthes
without harm. Even Homer knew that weeds do not perish
and the rabble survives. But this does not help the poor gnat.
There are many wily plants of the kind mentioned, and alto-
gether there are a few hundred carnivorous vegetables. The
same hidden malice lies in all of them, the same deceit and
falsehood. A lively insect settles on them; hungry, thirsty
and defenceless it sits down at the hospitable table with complete trust and freedom from care. And at once it is set upon

and strangled by thugs hiding in the inn. The gang surrounds it and crushes it. We know that this happens in our
familiar sundew, the "gang of thugs" being the ciliary hairs
on its treacherous tongue. The acids they conceal dissolve
the victim and the plant absorbs it.'

'Throughout nature there runs the dread of danger. It is
hard to believe that death is something "natural" when one
observes the caution of wild animals great and small, the
timid prudence of birds and the shyness of fish. "Divine"
nature everywhere presents the same picture, the frog slowly
swallowed by the snake, the wasps biting their victims' heads
and paralysing them so as to keep them alive as fresh meat:
victims victimizing their own victims. The right of the
stronger is the law of nature: "Into my power you must fall,
because I'm big and you are small."'

26. CONCLUSION

We have come to the end of this book and have not yet
raised the questions of the beginning or the end of this present
world, but instead have been occupied exclusively with its
present condition. But the questions inevitably arise as to
how this condition has come about, through what stages of
development has the world passed already, and where will this
development take us in the future? This whole complex of
questions has been deliberately kept out of this volume, for
before we can deal with them we must pay careful attention
to the present state of the world in which we live and set it in
relation to belief in God. Then, in a later volume, we can
look at the world's past history and at the problem of its
future. For these wider questions we have acquired certain
decisively important points of view in the volume which is
now finished. We have come to see, from many sides, the
basic forms of reality, the spaces in which they stand, and
the structural laws to which they are subject. This 'thinking
in spaces' to which we have been led suggests one particular
question which is provoked by the study of these spaces and
the basic forms of being. We saw that the entire real world
which is around us is subject in all its realms to a funda-

mental law which eastern religions and philosophies have always set exclusively at their centre, namely the fundamental law of polarity, to which space and time, as well as the conflict between the wholeness-structures of organic life, are alike subject. It has appeared in the course of our exposition that the world's suffering, and the struggle for existence between the structures which enjoy wholeness, have their deepest roots in this basic form of polarity. In eastern religions the notion occasionally crops up that the whole of this reality has fallen from an original condition where there was no such continual cleavage between polar phenomena, and that therefore the whole of reality is now in a state of suffering and pain and is vainly seeking a way out. In late Jewish apocalyptic we first meet the clearly expressed notion that it is not particular sufferings and imperfections which are responsible for the sorrow of the world, but rather the fundamental form under which the whole of the present world stands, namely the form of time, which has transformed the whole of existence into a restless flight from moment to moment. Hölderlin's poetry expresses the same attitude. This has given rise to old questions. Was the world always in this restless condition and will it remain in this state of unfulfilment? Or has it been pitchforked into its present destiny out of an original state which it once enjoyed, and will the time come when it will be rescued from its present condition? This is to state the problem which the biblical view of world-creation, world-development and world-consummation is chiefly concerned to expose at the root of all questions about the whence and whither of reality. This is a problem which we can deal with only in a separate volume, and we intend to do so because, even as regards the present, everything depends in practice on whether we are caught for ever, and the whole world with us, in this cosmic form of polarity, or whether there is an emancipation from this prison as Paul proclaimed in Romans 8.

If the first of these alternatives is true, the world's situation is absolutely without hope, because in its details and as a whole it stands under the shadow of an insoluble riddle. In the second case there is hope for a better future, and this hope is the light which falls upon the present state of affairs from a world to come, despite all present suffering. Life has a meaning, and the greatest suffering may be endured joyfully in the light of the future only when this light of the hope of redemption shines about us. This being so, it is our duty in the final volume to ask if there is anything to be found in the present state of nature which may tell us whether we are moving into the night, or whether, on the other hand, the facts of our present world-condition permit us, despite all suffering and all apparent meaninglessness, to hope for a brighter future.

INDEX OF NAMES

INDEX OF NAMES

261